Off to Adventure!

THEME 1

Off to Adventure!

Reader's Library Selection 1, *The Lunch Room*
To accompany Anthology Selection 1, *The Lost and Found*
Comprehension Skill: Sequence of Events

Reader's Library Selection 2, *Sacagawea*
To accompany Anthology Selection 2, *The Ballad of Mulan*
Comprehension Skill: Making Inferences

Reader's Library Selection 3, *A Great Day for Snorkeling*
To accompany Anthology Selection 3, *The Waterfall*
Comprehension Skill: Cause and Effect

The Lunch Room

by Rustie Arnott

illustrated by
Will Terry

THE LUNCH ROOM

by Rustie Arnott
illustrated by
Will Terry

Strategy Focus

Stan and Carmen want something else for dessert. What will they get? As you read, stop now and then to **summarize** each part of the story.

Responding

THINK ABOUT THE SELECTION

1. Which part of the school lunches do Carmen and Stan not like?

2. What are three things that happen when Stan and Carmen are in the different lunch room? Tell them in the right order.

WHAT HAPPENS NEXT?

Copy the chart on a piece of paper. Then fill it in for all the events in the story. Be sure to put them in the right order.

Event 1	Stan and Carmen both say "Yuk!" about the apples.
Event 2	They ask LouBelle for sweets for dessert.
Event 3	?
Event 4	?

Stan and Carmen sat in the lunch room. "Apples again," they both cried. "Yuk!"

Back in the *real* lunch room, Carmen and Stan grabbed two apples. They took giant bites. They were glad to have something good for dessert.

"Why can't we have good desserts?" asked Stan.

"Yeah, like Ring Rings, and YoHos, and Krispy Kat Bars," said Carmen.

They were getting sick! They had to get out! They jumped in the bin. It started to spin.

"They'll make your teeth fall out," said the lunch lady. Her name was LouBelle.

LouBelle kept the sweets coming.
"No more!" cried Stan and Carmen.

5A

THE LUNCH ROOM/Selection 1

"We never get anything we want," said Stan.

"An apple is a good thing," said LouBelle.

"Won't our teeth fall out?" asked Carmen.

"Not in *this* lunch room," said LouBelle.

Stan bit into his apple. There was a worm! Carmen laughed. Milk splashed on the floor.

9

LouBelle gave them cakes and ice cream! They got Ring Rings, YoHos and Krispy Kat Bars!

16

7A

"Stan-leee! Car-men!" called Lou Belle. "You two get a mop and clean that up."

"What'll you have? What'll you have?" said a voice. It was LouBelle! She *really* looked different.

Stan and Carmen looked into the mop room. "I don't see a mop," said Carmen.

The bin landed with a thud. Carmen and Stan were in the lunch room. But it was much different.

14

9A

"Maybe it's in here," said Stan.
He jumped into the bin. Carmen jumped in too.

The bin started to spin! It started to fall!
"What's going on?" yelled Stan.

Sacagawea

by Kana Riley

illustrated by Ron Himler

11A

Sacagawea

by Kana Riley

illustrated by Ron Himler

Strategy Focus

How will Sacagawea help Lewis and Clark on their long adventure? **Monitor** how well you understand the events. Reread to **clarify** parts that seem unclear.

Think About the Selection

1 Whom does Sacagawea help?

2 Why do you think Sacagawea thought of her home?

Making Inferences

Use a chart to help you make inferences about Sacagawea. Make another chart like this to tell how Sacagawea feels about going home.

Story Clue	What I Know from My Own Life
Sacagawea saves the food and supplies in wild waters.	I know wild waters can be dangerous.

Inference

Sacagawea is brave.

Sacagawea (Sack-ah-jah-**wee**-ah) sat in the boat with her baby. She was on a long journey home.

23

BRITISH CANADA

MISSISSIPPI RIVER

ST LOUIS

MISSOURI RIVER

LEWIS & CLARK JOURNEY

PLATTE RIVER

ARKANSAS RIVER

RED RIVER

NEW ORLEANS

GULF OF MEXICO

COLUMBIA RIVER

SNAKE RIVER

FT CLATSOP

PACIFIC OCEAN

Lewis and Clark went all the way to the Pacific Ocean. Sacagawea was with them. Together they had crossed the American West and soared into history.

38

Sacagawea/Selection 2

13A

Sacagawea thought about her home. It was the beautiful land of the Shoshone (Show-**show**-nee) people.

Then Lewis and Clark went on with their journey. They still needed Sacagawea's help. She went with them.

24

37

14A

The chief gave horses to the explorers. He made sure that the Shoshone treated them well.

When Sacagawea was a child, there had been a war. She had been taken far from her home.

36

25

15A

Now Sacagawea was going west with two explorers, Lewis and Clark.

Sacagawea spoke for Lewis and Clark. She told her brother about their great journey.

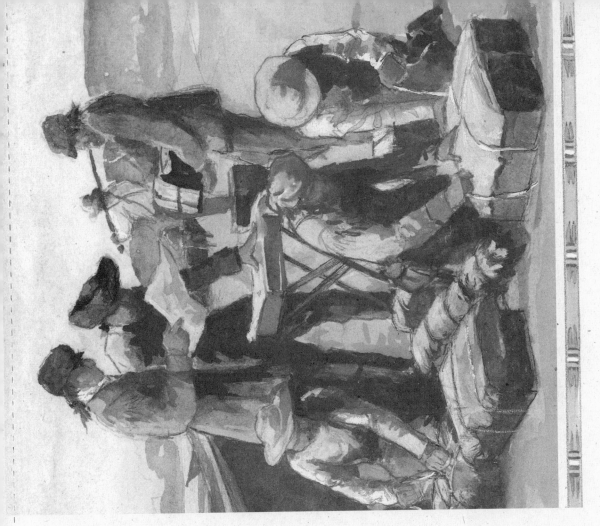

"Captain Lewis and Captain Clark need our help,"
Sacagawea's husband told her.

27

The Shoshone chief welcomed her. When
Sacagawea saw him, she burst into tears. It was her
brother!

34

17A

Sacagawea helped in many ways. She found meals of berries and nuts.

At long last, Sacagawea would see her people. She danced with joy.

28

33

18A

In wild waters, Sacagawea saved the explorers' food and supplies.

29

One day, Sacagawea knew she was home. "Shoshone country," she told Lewis and Clark.

32

19A

Lewis and Clark named a river for Sacagawea. They called it Birdwoman's River.

For weeks, Lewis and Clark raced down rushing rivers. Like a hawk, Sacagawea watched over them.

30

31

A GREAT DAY FOR SNORKELING

by Nuria Martín

illustrated by Cathy Diefendorf

A GREAT DAY FOR SNORKELING

by Nuria Martin
illustrated by Cathy Diefendorf

Strategy Focus

Will Grandma like snorkeling? Read the story carefully and try to **predict** what will happen.

Responding

Think About the Selection

1 At the beginning of the story, who says she wants to stay on the boat and read?

2 Why did Grandma jump in the water?

Cause and Effect

Copy the chart on a piece of paper. Then write one cause and one effect to fill in the chart.

Cause	Effect
There was a big splash.	The water got cloudy.
A dark shape was moving closer.	?
?	The girl yelled, "Grandma, help!"

"It's a great day for snorkeling," I said.

"It's a great day for a boat ride," said Grandma.

Grandma pointed at the blue and yellow fish.
I could tell what she was thinking.
"What a great day for snorkeling!"

A GREAT DAY FOR SNORKELING/Selection 3

"Grandma, you'll love snorkeling," I said.
She was afraid to try it. I could tell.

24A

"I thought snorkeling was for pigs!" I said.
"I guess I changed my mind," she said.
We both laughed. Then we dove back under.

"Snorkeling sounds like something pigs do!" she said. "I'll just stay on the boat and read."

"I thought you were a shark," I said.
"That's because I swim like a fish," said Grandma.

54

25A   A GREAT DAY FOR SNORKELING/Selection 3

A GREAT DAY FOR SNORKELING/Selection 3

"But you said you'd try!" I told her.

"I guess I changed my mind," she said.

26A

It was Grandma!

The boat stopped. I pulled on my mask.

"I'm going in without you," I said.

27A

"Grandma, help!" I yelled again.

"Here I am!" said a voice next to me.

A GREAT DAY FOR SNORKELING/Selection 3

The water looked deep and dark.
But I jumped right in.

But she wasn't there! I started paddling fast.
Something grabbed my leg!

The water felt warm as a hug.
I saw colorful fish all around.

47

I popped my head out of the water.
"Grandma!" I shouted back at the boat.

50

Suddenly there was a big splash.
The water got cloudy. I saw only bubbles.

A dark shape was moving closer. My heart
pounded fast. Was it a shark?

Celebrating Traditions

THEME 2

Celebrating Traditions

Reader's Library Selection 1, *Grandma's Table*
To accompany Anthology Selection 1, *The Keeping Quilt*
Comprehension Skill: Author's Viewpoint

Reader's Library Selection 2, *The Mask Makers*
To accompany Anthology Selection 2, *Anthony Reynoso:
  Born to Rope*
Comprehension Skill: Categorize and Classify

Reader's Library Selection 3, *The Weaver's Gift*
To accompany Anthology Selection 3, *The Talking Cloth*
Comprehension Skill: Noting Details

Reader's Library Selection 4, *Festival in Valencia*
To accompany Anthology Selection 4, *Dancing Rainbows*
Comprehension Skill: Topic, Main Idea, and Supporting Details

Grandma's Table

by Penina Adelman

illustrated by John F. Martin

Grandma's Table

by Penina Adelman
illustrated by John F. Martin

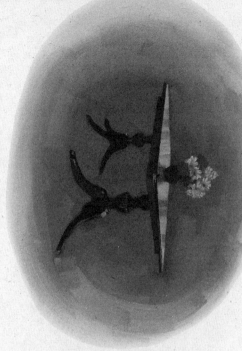

Strategy Focus

What is special about Grandma's table? As you read, **evaluate** the author's memories about her grandmother.

Responding

Think About the Selection

1 What does Grandma do to her table every day?

2 How does the author feel about her Grandpa? Why do you think that?

What Does the Author Feel?

Copy this chart on a piece of paper. Then fill in one more detail from the story that supports what the author feels.

The Author Feels	I know this from these details in the story.
When she was a girl, she liked visiting Grandma.	The author says it was "a great place to be."
The author loved the food that Grandma made.	?

21

Every Friday night, my husband, my children, and I eat at our family table. The table once belonged to my grandmother.

5

3B

"We don't love school *all* the time, either!" say my children. Everyone laughs. Then I tell them more stories around Grandma's table.

20

Grandma's Table/Selection 1

5

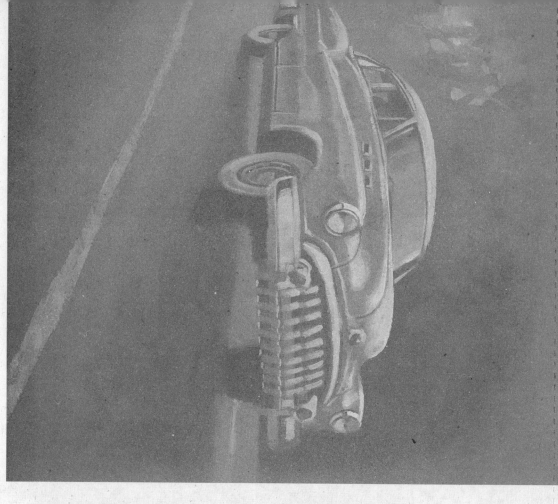

When I was a girl, Grandma lived far away.
My family drove a day and a night to visit her.

"I don't love it *all* the time, Grandma,"
I said. Everyone laughed. They knew I was
joking.

"Later my mother and I laughed about it," said Grandma. "But it wasn't funny that I never went back to school. I'm glad my grandchild loves school."

18

When we got there, I ran right into Grandma's arms. Everyone got a big hug from Grandma. It was a great place to be.

7

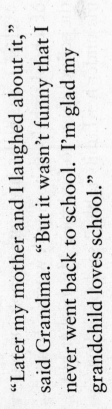

8

Then we went into the dining room.
The table was piled high with wonderful food.
"Sit," said Grandma. "Eat."

"When I was eight, my mother took me out of school to help at home. A woman from the school came to find me. My mother hid me under her family table," said Grandma.

Then Grandma told another story.

We ate. We laughed. Grandma told stories.

16

9

7B

"I'll never forget the day Grandpa brought this table from my parents' home," Grandma began one story.

We all got quiet for a moment, missing Grandpa. I still miss him today.

Grandma got quiet after that story. "I miss Grandpa," she said. "He loved our family meals. Remember how he led the Passover seder?"

"We had such a time getting it up the stairs," she said.

14

11

"I've polished it every day since then," Grandma said. "I still polish it every day."

The table was as shiny as a butterscotch candy.

The Mask Makers

by Veronica Freeman Ellis
illustrated by Rosanne Kaloustian

The Mask Makers

by Veronica Freeman Ellis
illustrated by Rosanne Kaloustian

Strategy Focus

A boy goes to Africa to learn a family tradition. As you read, think of **questions** you could ask a friend about this story.

Responding

Think About the Selection

1. Where does the boy live? Where does his Grandfather live?

2. Tell about two ways the family uses the masks.

Categorize and Classify

In the story, the family members are in two different places. Find some of the things that happen in each place. Write them in a chart like this.

Things That Happen in Liberia	Things That Happen in Boston
Grandfather makes masks.	There is a neighborhood fair.

This summer we're visiting my grandfather.
He lives in Monrovia (Mon-**RO**-vee-ah), Liberia
(Lie-**BEAR**-ee-ah). Liberia is a country in Africa.

23

13B

Soon many people gather around my grandfather.
"Once upon a time," he begins.

38

The Mask Makers/Selection 2

Here we are in my grandfather's village.
My dad used to live there when he was a boy.

He chooses his favorite one.
Then he uses it to tell a story.

My grandfather makes masks.
He carves each mask from one block of wood.

25

But I'm happy anyway.
At least my grandfather likes my masks.

36

The Mask Makers/Selection 2

15B

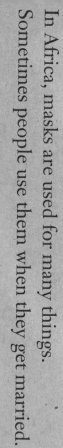

In Africa, masks are used for many things. Sometimes people use them when they get married.

People want to buy my dad's masks. They don't want to buy mine!

Sometimes they use them when a baby is born.
And sometimes they use them when telling stories.

27

My family sells masks that my dad and I made.
My masks don't look as good as my dad's.

34

The Mask Makers/Selection 2

My dad knows how to carve masks too.
His father, my grandfather, taught him.
Now my grandfather teaches me.

Today there's a neighborhood fair.
The fair has rides, crafts, and food.
We're raising money for a playground.

28

33

I choose a block of wood.
My grandfather shows me what to do.

32

A year has passed.
My grandfather is visiting us in Boston.

After many days I have a mask.
I use my mask and tell a story.

My grandfather uses his storytelling mask too.
We all have a good time.

The Weaver's Gift

by Lee S. Justice

illustrated by Rosanne Kaloustian

The Weaver's Gift

by Lee S. Justice
illustrated by Rosanne Kaloustian

Strategy Focus

A Navajo boy tells how his people make rugs. Stop and **summarize** parts of the story as you read. It will help you keep track of the story.

Responding

Think About the Selection

1. Among the Navajo people, who teaches the skill of weaving rugs?

2. What details tell you about Aunt Gloria's visit?

Noting Details

Copy the web on a piece of paper. Then write details that complete the idea.

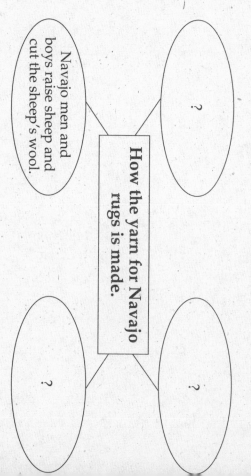

How the yarn for Navajo rugs is made.

?

?

Navajo men and boys raise sheep and cut the sheep's wool.

?

This is the land of the Navajo. (**NAHV**-eh-ho) people. Long ago, sheep were brought here.

23B

Then I said, "This rug is part of my family. That is why it is so beautiful to me."

The Weaver's Gift/Selection 3

The Navajo began raising the sheep. They learned to weave with yarn made from the sheep's wool.

I held up a rug and said, "This rug was woven by the grandmother of the grandmother of my mother."

Everyone clapped.

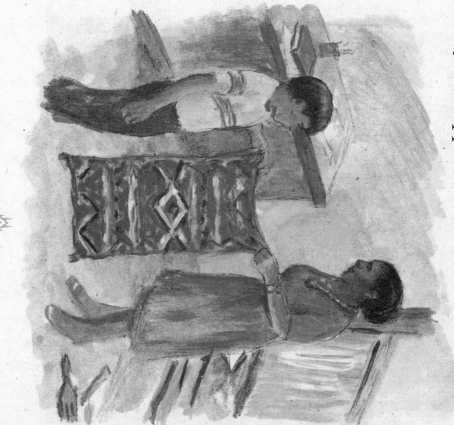

Girls learned to weave from their mothers.
When the girls grew up, they taught their daughters.

25B

My classmates tried weaving.

Then Aunt Gloria said to the class, "Henry has something to show you."

The Weaver's Gift/Selection 3

Men and boys helped too. They raised the sheep. They cut the sheep's wool.

Aunt Gloria set up her loom. She showed us how she weaves.

The weaver combed out the wool. She pushed and pulled, using cards with points.

27B

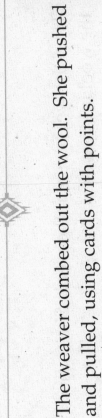I know these things because I learned them from my Aunt Gloria. She is a weaver. Aunt Gloria came to my school today.

The Weaver's Gift/Selection 3

Then the weaver spun the wool. She turned the wool into yarn.

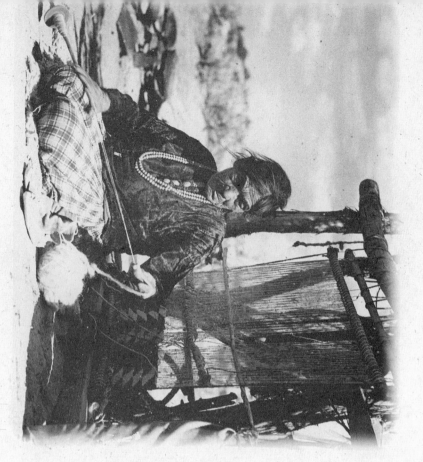

Navajo weaving began long ago. It is still going on today.

After that, the weaver gathered plants. Plants were boiled to make dyes. The dyes were used to color the yarn.

29B

A weaver sang as she sat at the loom. Her songs were woven into the rug. The rug held her thoughts too. It became a part of her.

50

The Weaver's Gift/Selection 3

The weaver set up her loom. In her mind she formed a picture of what she would make. She began weaving the picture into her rug.

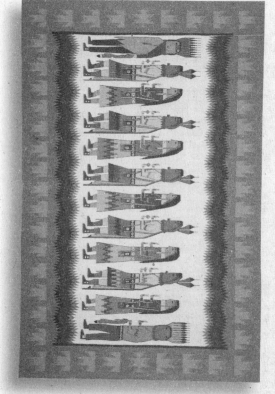

Rugs had many kinds of patterns. Each pattern held special meanings.

Festival in Valencia

by Anne Miranda

illustrated by Robert Casilla

Festival in Valencia

by Anne Miranda
illustrated by
Robert Casilla

Strategy Focus

What are those funny statues in Valencia? **Monitor** your reading. Reread to **clarify** any parts you don't understand.

Responding

Think About the Selection

1. What is a *falla* ?

2. Besides making a *falla*, groups in Valencia celebrate this festival in other ways. Write ways they celebrate.

Main Idea and Details

Copy the chart on a piece of paper. Write two supporting details for the second main idea.

Main Ideas	Supporting Details
Many groups plan for *Las Fallas.*	1. The groups hire artists to make *fallas* that will win prizes. 2. They show off their *fallas* in a parade all over Valencia.
At the festival's end, the *fallas* are burned.	1. ? 2. ?

Ana is visiting her cousin Rocío in Valencia, Spain.

It's time for the yearly festival called *Las Fallas* (**LAS FAH**-yahs).

59

Next year, their new *fallas* will be just as wonderful!

74

Ana has been to many Mexican festivals at home in Texas.

Rocío says that *Las Fallas* will be very different!

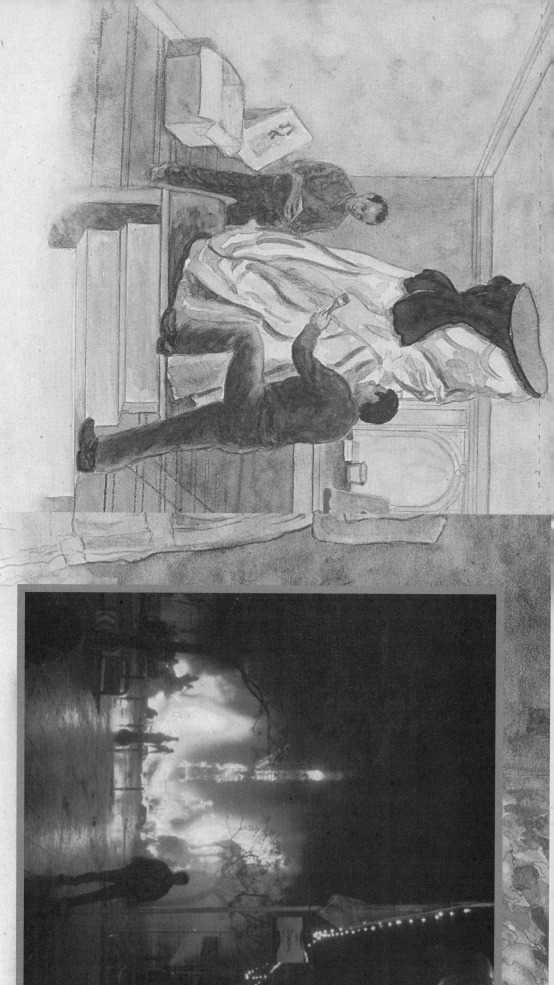

Everyone else is cheering, but Ana is shocked!

Rocío explains that the *fallas* are always burned. It is the tradition.

A *falla* (**FAH**-yah) is a big statue. It's made of special paper called *papier-mâché* (**PAY**-per ma-**SHAY**).

Groups of people in Valencia often hire artists to make *fallas*.

61

On the last night, Ana is in for a big surprise. First, the fire fighters spray the buildings. This is so the buildings won't burn. Then they set fire to the *fallas* all over Valencia!

72

Ana's family belongs to one of these groups.

Their *falla* is in pieces on this truck.

Next comes a parade. People in the group love to show off their winning *falla*.

This year, Rocío's mother has been chosen to pick up the prize for the whole group.

70

Everyone helps put up the *falla*. First, they unload the pieces. Then they put the pieces together.

63

37B

All over Valencia, other groups are also putting up *fallas.*

38B

Many people have special festival costumes. The people in Ana's family have had their costumes for many years. There's an extra one for Ana too.

69

Fallas often make people laugh. Many *fallas* poke fun at stories in the news. Some are made to look like famous people in Valencia.

65

39B

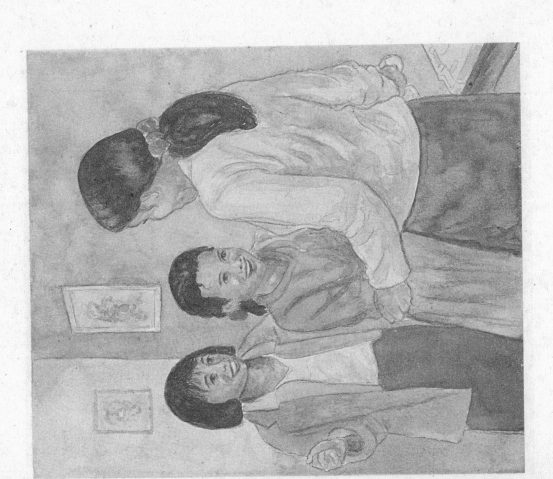

The next morning, Ana's family gets exciting news. Their group's *falla* has won a prize!

68

Festival in Valencia/Selection 4

Ana and her family go to see other *fallas*. This huge one is in the main plaza.

The group has a party while the *fallas* are being judged. The best *fallas* will win prizes.

HOUGHTON MIFFLIN
Reading
A Legacy of Literacy

Incredible Stories

THEME 3

Incredible Stories

Reader's Library Selection 1, *Robocat*
To accompany Anthology Selection 1, *Dogzilla*
Comprehension Skill: Fantasy/Realism

Reader's Library Selection 2, *The Dragon of Krakow*
To accompany Anthology Selection 2, *The Mysterious
  Giant of Barletta*
Comprehension Skill: Following Directions

Reader's Library Selection 3, *My Green Thumb*
To accompany Anthology Selection 3, *Raising Dragons*
Comprehension Skill: Drawing Conclusions

Reader's Library Selection 4, *Luna*
To accompany Anthology Selection 4, *The Garden of Abdul Gasazi*
Comprehension Skill: Story Structure

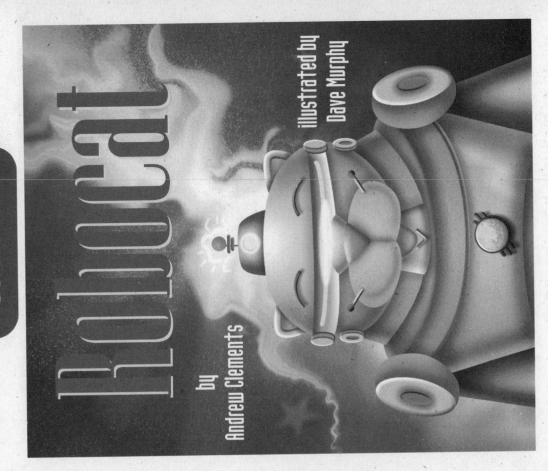

Robocat

by
Andrew Clements

illustrated by
Dave Murphy

Robocat

by Andrew Clements

illustrated by Dave Murphy

Strategy Focus

As you read the story, stop once in a while to **evaluate** how the author shows that Robocat is a fantasy cat.

Responding

Thinking About the Selection

1. What are Patch Rabbit and the Hoppers doing in the garden?

2. Tell about one part of the story that could really happen and one part that couldn't.

Is It Real or Is It Fantasy?

There are some things a real cat can do and some things only a fantasy cat can do. Think of some of each of those things. Then write them on a chart like this.

Real cats can	Fantasy cats can
meow	talk

It was a beautiful summer day.
But something didn't feel right.
Robocat could smell crime
in the air.

Robocat said, "Not while Robocat's
watching!"

Patch smiled. "We can wait until you take
a catnap," he said.

20

Robocat looked between the rows of vegetables. He looked all around the garden.

Patch Rabbit said, "We will find a way out of here, I promise! And when we do, we will eat every vegetable in the garden!"

Then he said, "Someone's been tasting the turnips. Someone's been crunching the carrots. This looks like a job for Robocat!"

"And now we know the answer!" said Robocat. "Like I said, I have you. And now you are all going to spend some time with the chickens."

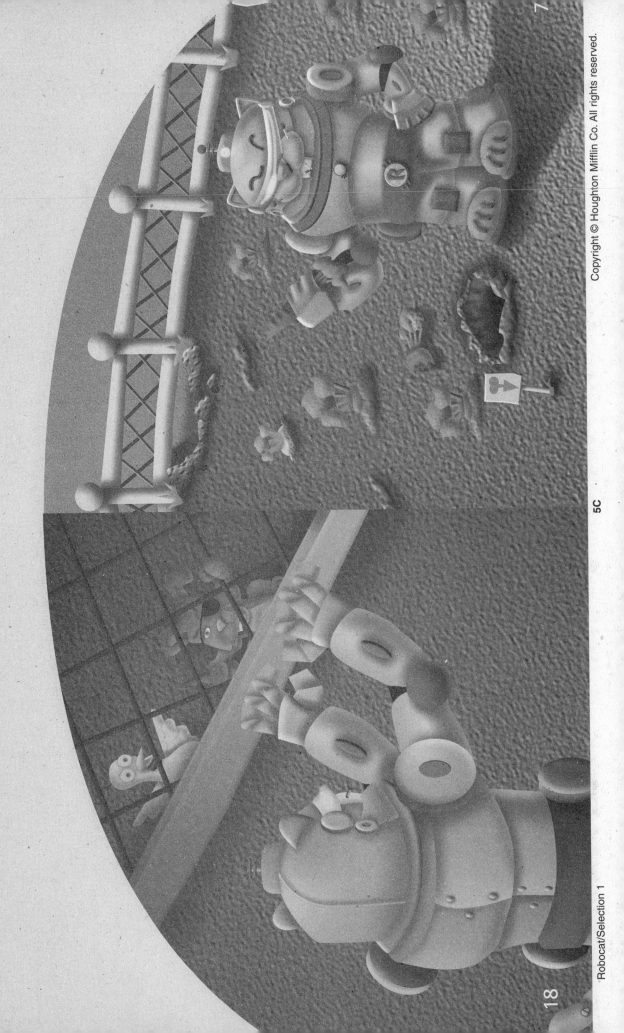

18

That night Robocat hid in a tree by the garden. He said, "These crooks don't have a chance."

Patch Rabbit said, "Not so fast, Tuna Breath. Do you have us or do we have you?"

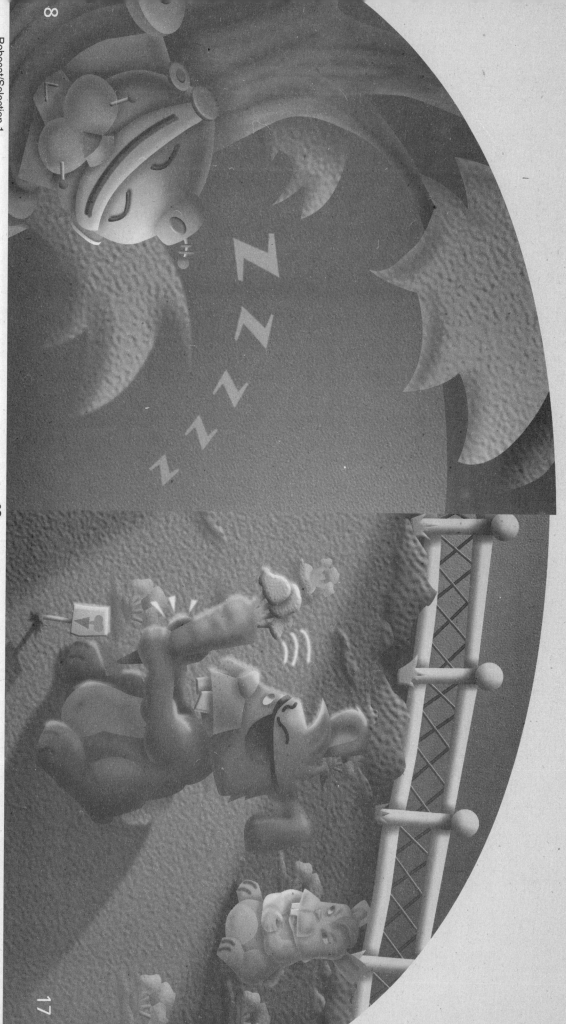

Robocat watched the garden all night long.
Well, almost all night long.

It was Patch Rabbit and the Hoppers!
Robocat said, "Paws up! I have you at last!"

9

16

7C

The next morning Robocat went down to the garden. More turnips and carrots were gone!

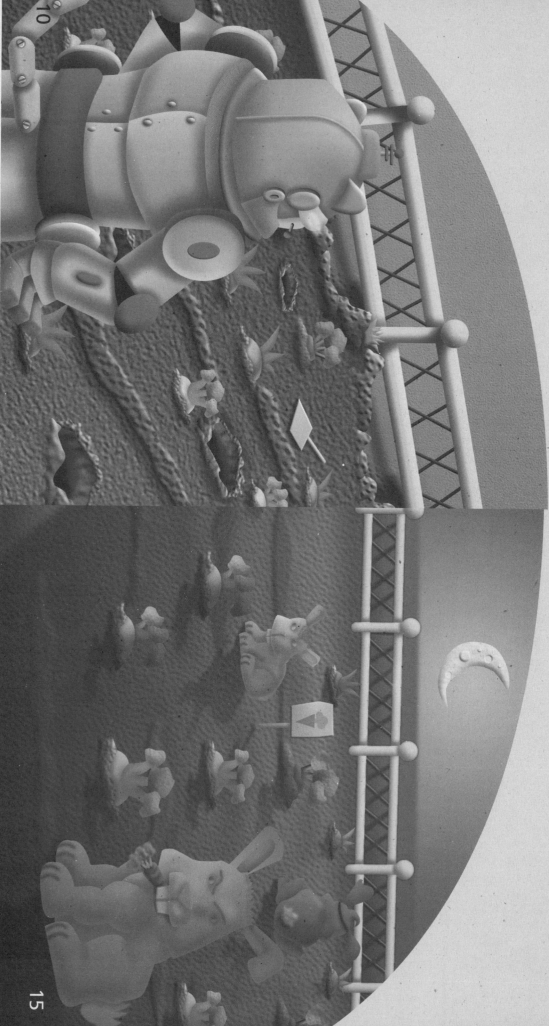

Suddenly Robocat flipped on his lights. He said, "You should be scared. I'm Robocat! Stay right where you are!"

That night, Robocat heard digging and nibbling. Someone saw Robocat. Someone laughed and said, "Would you look at that! I'm sooooo scared!"

14

Robocat saw holes, lots of holes, under the fence. He said, "Someone's been digging under the fence! Someone's been playing dirty!"

11

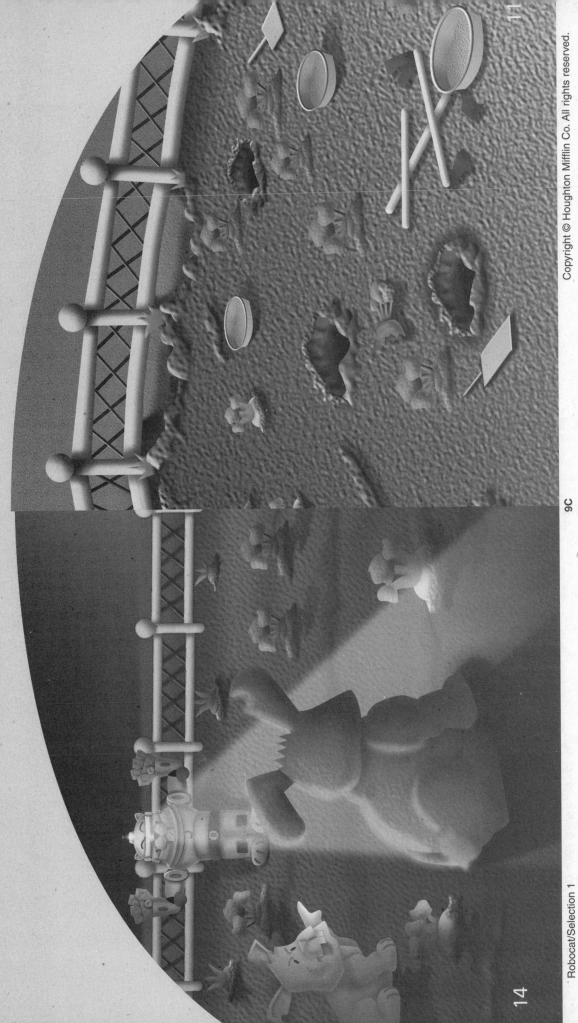

Robocat/Selection 1

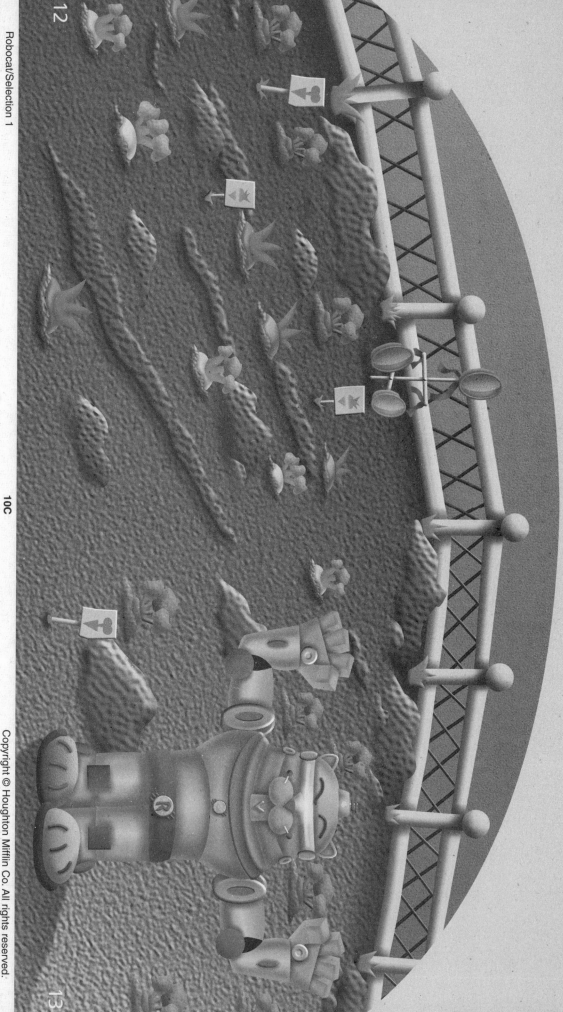

Robocat filled all the holes. Then he stood very still in the garden. He waited for something to happen.

"These crooks think they're pretty smart," he said. "But not when Robocat is on the case!"

The Dragon of Krakow

A Polish folktale

adapted by Maryann Dobeck
illustrated by Krystyna Stasiak

Selection 2

The Dragon of Krakow

A Polish folktale

adapted by Maryann Dobeck
illustrated by Krystyna Stasiak

Strategy Focus

A hungry dragon comes to town. As you read, think of **questions** to discuss.

Responding

Think About the Selection

1 What do Krakus and the villagers see when they go down to the river?

2 Give directions to the characters in the story, telling them what they must do each day.

Following Directions

Here are directions Krakus might have given the villagers. Copy them on a piece of paper in the order he would want them done.

Next, help me mix all the spicy food together.

Last, bake this spicy mixture in a pie.

First, bring me all your spicy food.

Long ago there was a little village in Poland that had no name. The people who lived there worked so hard, they had no time to think of one!

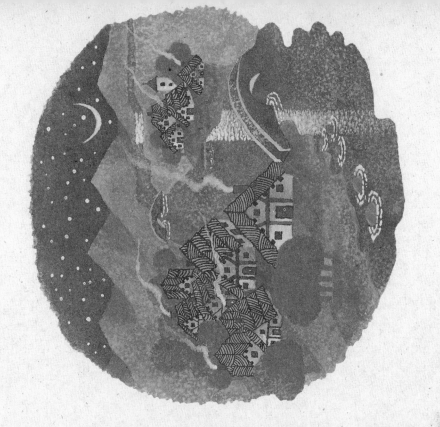

The dragon took off, never to be seen again. The villagers made Krakus their king. Then they named their village Krakow for the clever man who had saved one and all.

The Dragon of Krakow/Selection 2

Every morning a rooster crowed at the rising sun. When the villagers heard his "kru, kru, kru," they woke up.

The dragon ate the whole pie. But the hot, spicy food burned his insides. He roared, and the mountains shook. Then he nearly drank the river dry.

Krakus mixed all the food together. Then the baker baked it into a pie.

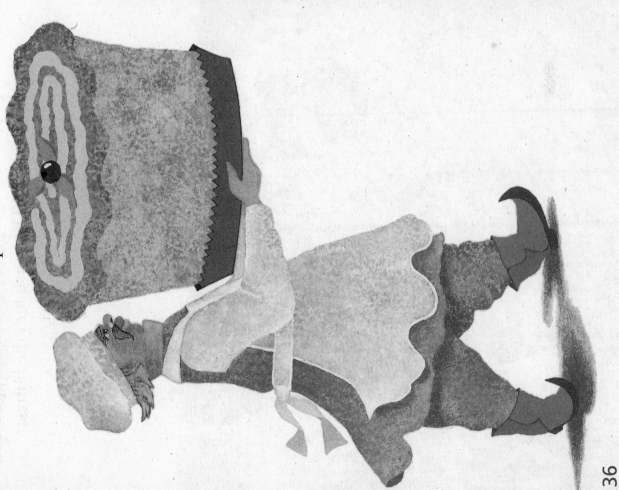

They had to get up very early because there was so much work to do.

15C

The farmer fed the pigs.
The milkmaid milked the cows.
The butcher made sausages.

Krakus asked the villagers for all their hot,
spicy foods. They gave him hot peppers and
hot mustard. They gave him the hottest
sausages in the land.

The baker made cakes, rolls, and pies.
The woodsman cut down trees.

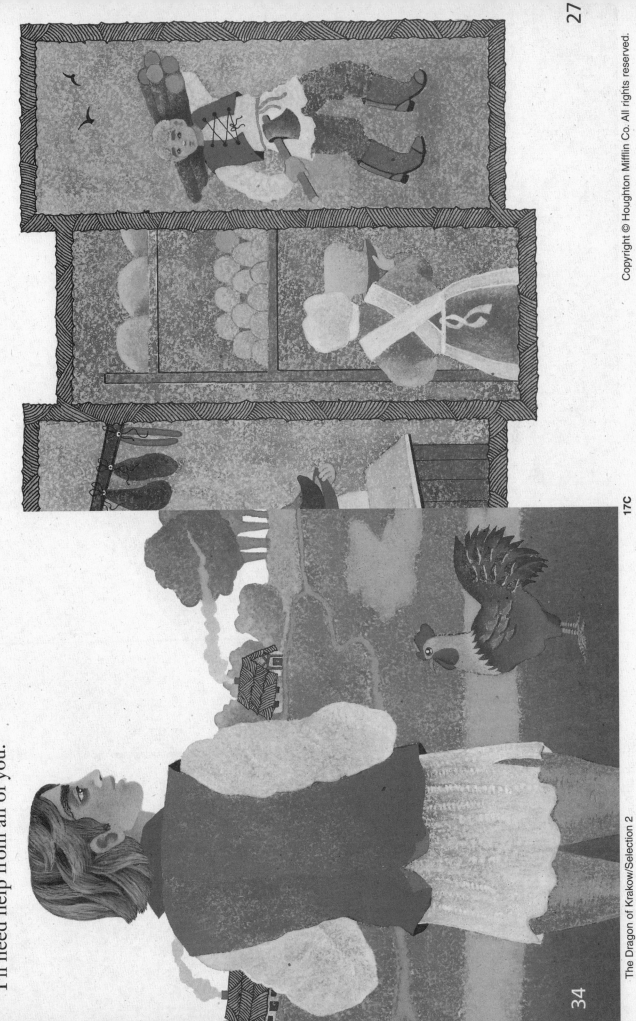

"What can we do?" cried the villagers.

"I have a plan," said Krakus. "Just do as I say.
I'll need help from all of you."

17C

The Dragon of Krakow/Selection 2

But one morning the rooster woke up late. Smoke covered everything. It blocked out the sun. Day was as black as night.

"I'm hungry!" roared the dragon. "Bring me the best foods in the land. Then make me your king, or I will eat you up!"

When the rooster saw the dark day and smelled the smoke, he began to crow. He crowed "kru, kru, kru" ten times louder than ever before. The villagers came out to see what was the matter.

On the edge of the river was a dragon. He was covered with scales. He had rows of long, pointy teeth. Flames and smoke came out of his mouth.

32

29

19C

The Dragon of Krakow/Selection 2

The villagers could see bright flames down by the river.

"The forest must be on fire!" yelled the woodsman.

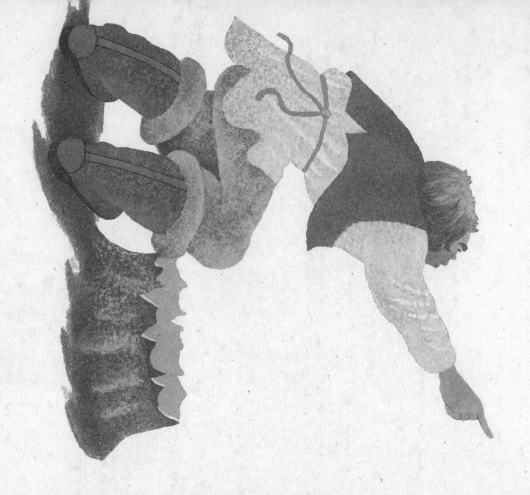

A young man named Krakus called out, "Follow me, and we will see!"

Krakus and the villagers went down to the river.

MY GREEN THUMB

by Maxine Effenson Chuck
illustrated by Mary GrandPré

MY GREEN THUMB

by Maxine Effenson Chuck
illustrated by Mary GrandPré

Strategy Focus

When Isador touches plants, amazing things happen. As you read, **predict** what Isador will do with his strange ability.

Responding

THINK ABOUT THE SELECTION

1 What happens to Isador's thumb?

2 What makes Isador believe that he is a special gardener?

USE CLUES TO DRAW A CONCLUSION

One way to think about drawing conclusions is to keep a chart like this. Copy the chart on a piece of paper. Then complete the chart by writing more clues that show how having a green thumb can sometimes be a problem.

Clues	Conclusion
He grows a carrot that bursts through the kitchen wall.	Isador's green thumb is very powerful. Sometimes that power causes problems.
?	
?	

My father is a gardener. And now, so am I.
Here's how it happened.

23C

The judges said they had never seen such a big pumpkin. They told me that someday I would be a great gardener. They didn't know that someday was already here!

56

MY GREEN THUMB/Selection 3

MY GREEN THUMB/Selection 3

One day I was helping my father in the garden. Suddenly it started raining. My thumb felt funny. I looked down and saw that it was green!

I picked out my best pumpkin and took it to the fair.

When the rain stopped, I helped my father with some tomato plants. In a flash, the tomatoes grew as big as pillows.

43

Now I was ready for pumpkins. I grew them big, but not too big.

54

"What's going on?" I asked my father. "I guess those tomatoes *really* needed water," my father said. I wasn't so sure.

At last, I learned how to control my thumb. I'd give a small green apple a little squeeze, and then BINGO. A large red apple sat in my hand.

So I grabbed a sunflower.
It grew as big as an umbrella!
Soon I was high above the garden.

Then I grew so many Brussels sprouts,
I had to eat them for a week. Yuck!

From up there, I picked a rose. It grew as big as a pizza. A bee feasted on the rose. The bee grew as big as a hummingbird!

Next, I tried an onion. It didn't grow as big as the carrot. But its smell was so strong, we cried our eyes out.

My mother was amazed.
She said, "Isador, let's not tell anyone about this."
My father said, "Yes, people won't understand."
I said, "But I want to show everyone what I can do."

50

I needed practice. I started with a carrot. I held the top. The carrot burst through my fingers. Then it burst through the kitchen wall.

"Well," said my father, "why don't you grow a pumpkin for the county fair? Then you can show what you can do without telling how you do it!"

It was a great idea. But it wasn't an easy one. Every pumpkin I grew got much too big to carry.

LUNA

by Philemon Sturges

illustrated by Suling Wang

LUNA

by Philemon Sturges

illustrated by Suling Wang

Strategy Focus

Saul has an unusual pet named Luna. As you read, **monitor** how well you follow what happens, and reread to **clarify** anything you don't understand.

Responding

Think About the Selection

1. What is Luna at the beginning of the story? What is she at the end?

2. What is Saul's problem at the beginning of the story? What is Saul's problem when he comes home from Grandpa's?

Story Structure

One way to look at the structure of a story is to make a story map. Copy this map on a piece of paper and then complete it.

STORY MAP

Beginning	Grandpa is sick, and Saul leaves his caterpillar, Luna, at home.
Middle	?
End	?

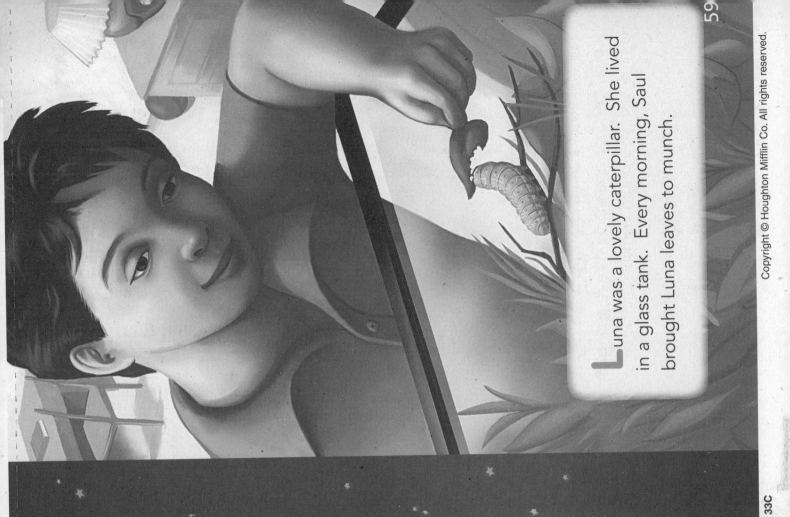

Luna was a lovely caterpillar. She lived in a glass tank. Every morning, Saul brought Luna leaves to munch.

33C

"I'm Luna," the moth seemed to say. "I've changed, that's all. But I'll always be your friend."

Then Luna flew into the moonlit night.

74

LUNA/Selection 4

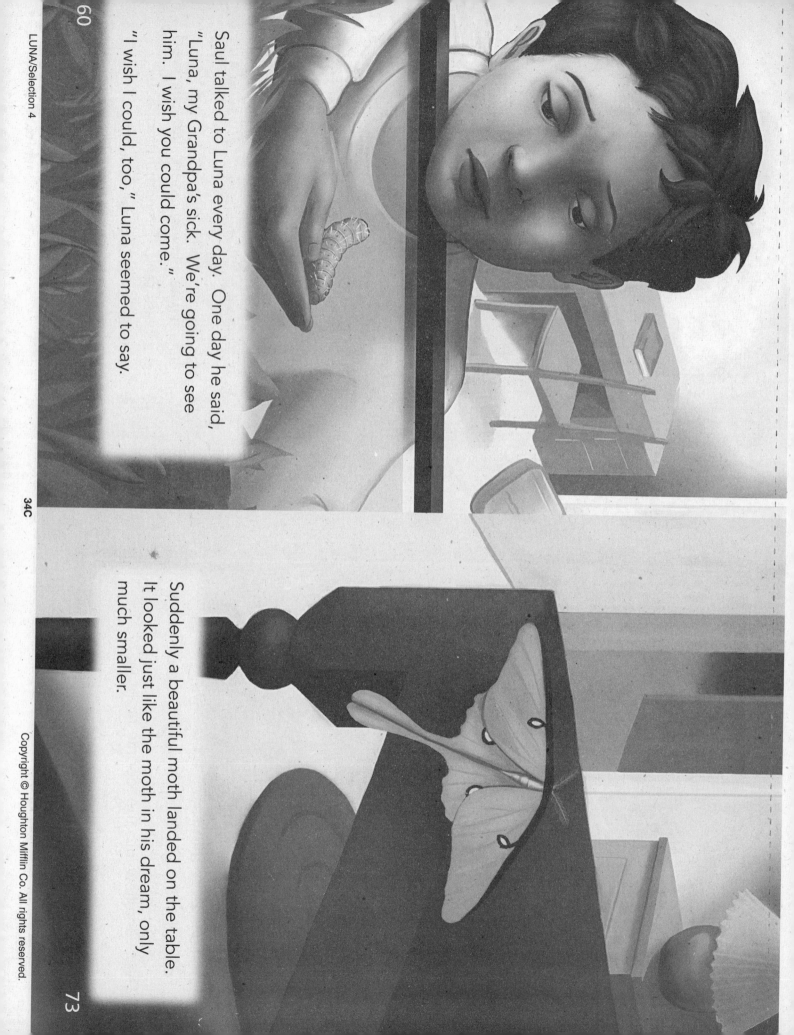

Saul talked to Luna every day. One day he said, "Luna, my Grandpa's sick. We're going to see him. I wish you could come."

"I wish I could, too," Luna seemed to say.

Suddenly a beautiful moth landed on the table. It looked just like the moth in his dream, only much smaller.

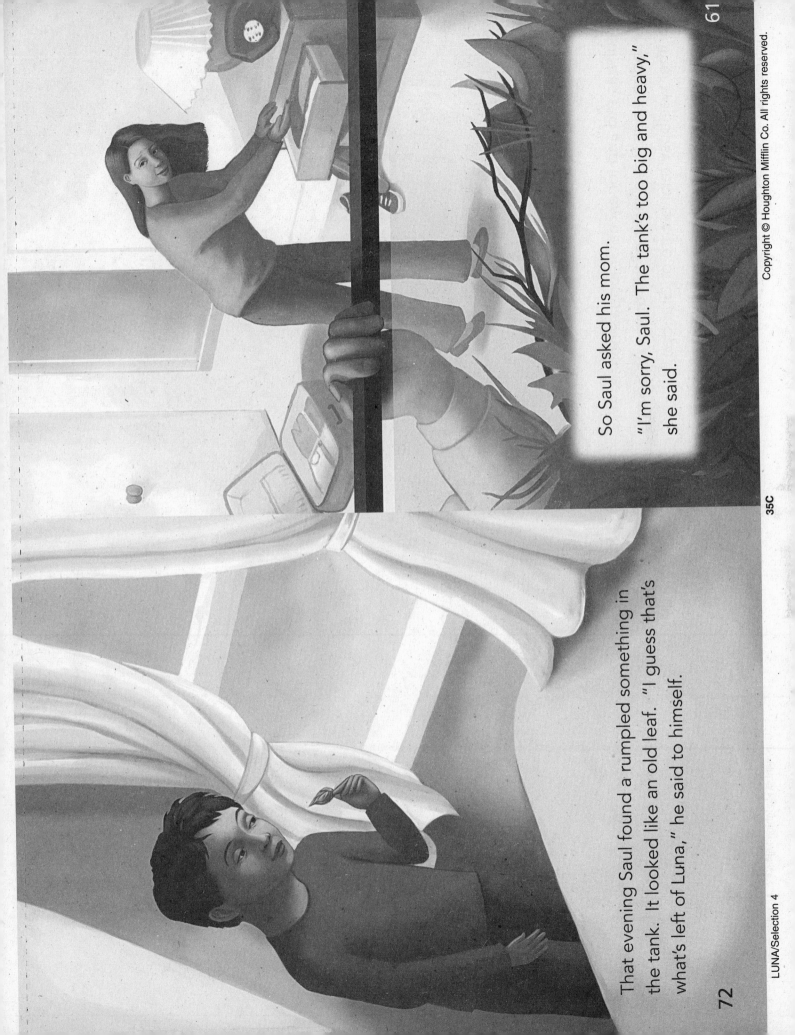

So Saul asked his mom.

"I'm sorry, Saul. The tank's too big and heavy," she said.

72

That evening Saul found a rumpled something in the tank. It looked like an old leaf. "I guess that's what's left of Luna," he said to himself.

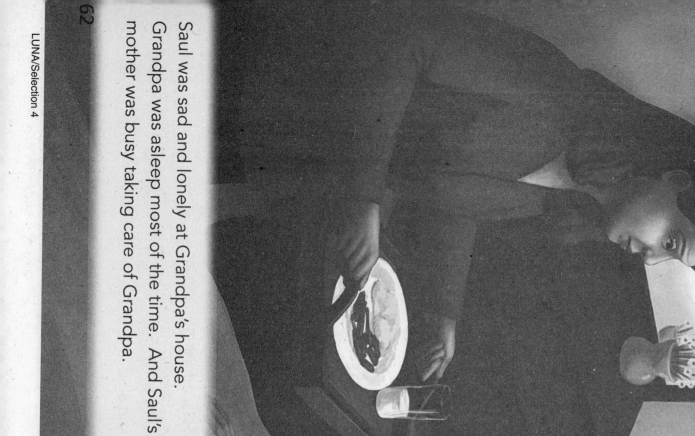

Saul was sad and lonely at Grandpa's house. Grandpa was asleep most of the time. And Saul's mother was busy taking care of Grandpa.

Then she smiled and said, "But sick people can get better! Grandpa just called. He took a long walk this morning."

Saul missed Luna. He wanted to tell her how lonely he was.

At breakfast Saul told his mother about the giant moth. Mom said, "You were dreaming. Moths don't carry people. And they can't fly to the moon!"

37C

70

LUNA/Selection 4

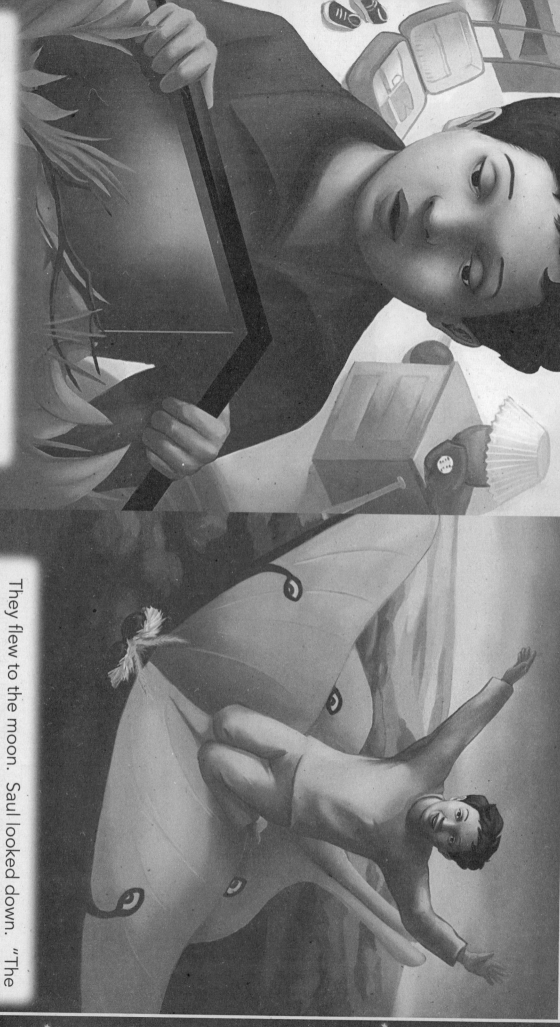

When they got home, Saul rushed in to see Luna. "Did you miss me?" he asked his caterpillar. Saul looked inside the tank.

They flew to the moon. Saul looked down. "The earth is magical!" he said. "So it is," said the moth.

Luna was gone. Saul looked all around his room.
No Luna. "Mom!" Saul cried. "Luna is gone!
Why did we have to go to Grandpa's?"

When the moon came to the top of the sky, Saul
woke up. A giant moth stood glowing in the
moonlight.

"Climb on my back," she said. "Let's go for a
ride."

Mom hugged Saul. Then she said, "Grandpa couldn't take care of himself. Luna can. She's probably outside having a great time. But I'm sure she misses you."

That night Saul watched the full moon rise and thought about Luna. Then he thought about Grandpa. And then he fell asleep.

HOUGHTON MIFFLIN
Reading
A Legacy of Literacy

Animal Habitats

THEME 4

Animal Habitats

Reader's Library Selection 1, *Dear Butterflies...*
To accompany Anthology Selection 1, *Nights of the Pufflings*
Comprehension Skill: Fact and Opinion

Reader's Library Selection 2, *Henry and the Fox*
To accompany Anthology Selection 2, *Seal Surfer*
Comprehension Skill: Compare/Contrast

Reader's Library Selection 3, *The Upside-Down Elephant*
To accompany Anthology Selection 3, *Two Days in May*
Comprehension Skill: Making Judgments

Dear Butterflies...

by Maryann Dobeck

illustrated by David Austin Clar

Dear Butterflies...

by Maryann Dobeck
illustrated by David Austin Clar

Strategy Focus

Can Julia's class find a way to save their butterflies? As you read, **evaluate** how the class solves the problem.

Think About the Selection

1. What are caterpillars?

2. Find a sentence from the story that tells a fact about the butterfly's diet and another that tells an opinion about it.

Fact and Opinion

Copy the chart on a piece of paper. Read the sentences. They are from the poster in the story. Then tell which sentences are facts and which are opinions.

Statement	Fact	Opinion
A small caterpillar comes from the egg.	✓	
Its stripes are pretty.		✓
The caterpillar grows bigger.	?	?
Its skin falls off.	?	?
This looks icky!	?	?
Out comes a monarch butterfly!	?	?
It is really beautiful!	?	?

That night Julia wrote in her journal.

Dear Butterflies,
I hope that you are as
happy in your new home as
I am in mine.

Love,
Julia Rodriguez

"Class," said Mrs. Evans. "Please show Julia around." Julia was starting her school year a little late. She had just moved to a new home.

Julia pointed to a glass tank. "What are they?" she asked. "They look funny."

"They are monarch butterflies," said Seth.

"They don't *look* like butterflies," said Julia.

Julia's father came to class on his way to work. Julia gave him the box.

"I'll be very careful with them," he said. "By the end of the day, I'll set them free in Mexico."

Hector said, "Right now, they're called *caterpillars*. But soon they will turn into butterflies."

By the time the caterpillars turned into butterflies, the class had a plan. They put the butterflies in a box with tiny holes.

Each caterpillar had yellow, black, and white stripes.

"Eww!" said Julia. She watched the caterpillars eat the leaves. "Do they eat grass too?"

"We can't put butterflies in the mail," said Kim.

"No," said Julia. "But maybe we can fly them on an airplane. I'll ask my father. He's a pilot."

"No," said Michael. "They only eat milkweed leaves."

"Ugh!" said Julia. "How boring!"

7D

"We've been trying to think of ways to help them," said Kim. "So they won't die."

"Maybe we could mail them to Mexico," said Emily.

16

"No, they really like those leaves," Seth laughed. "It's like having pizza all the time!"

Mrs. Evans went on. "We just got the caterpillars last week. It's too late in the fall for them to make the trip. They won't find enough food along the way."

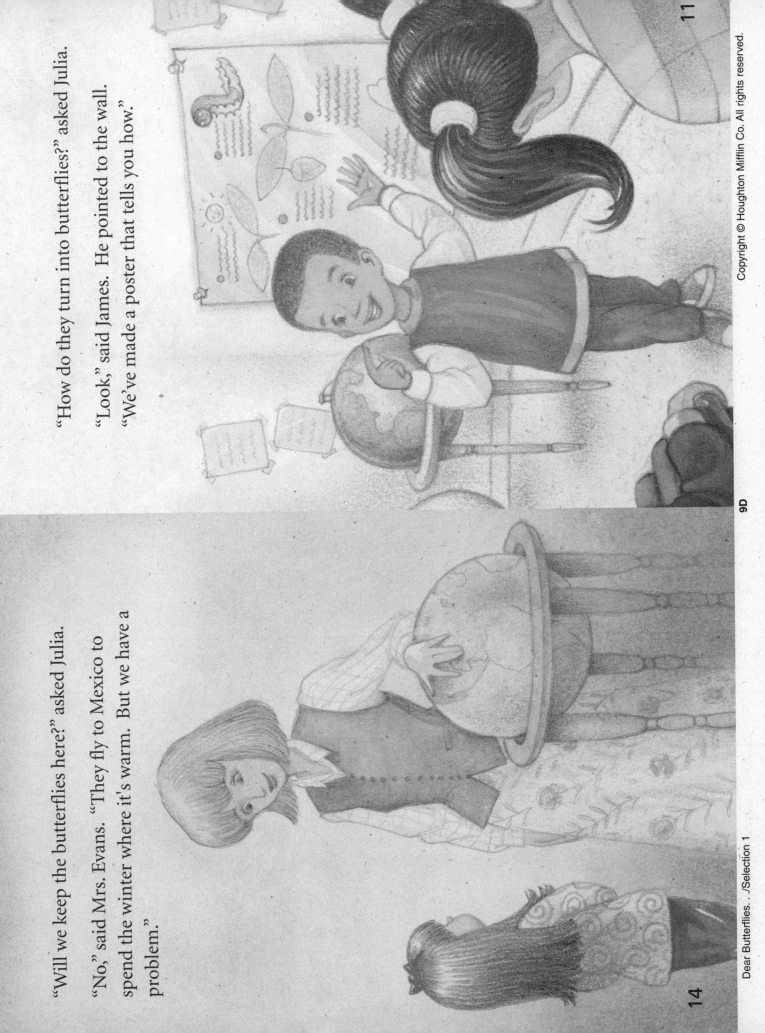

"How do they turn into butterflies?" asked Julia.

"Look," said James. He pointed to the wall. "We've made a poster that tells you how."

11

"Will we keep the butterflies here?" asked Julia.

"No," said Mrs. Evans. "They fly to Mexico to spend the winter where it's warm. But we have a problem."

14

9D

1. In late summer, the monarch butterfly lays her tiny white egg on a milkweed plant.

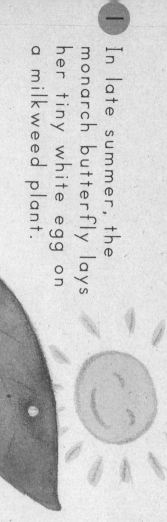

2. A small caterpillar comes from the egg. Its stripes are pretty.

3. The caterpillar eats the milkweed leaves.

4. The caterpillar grows. Its skin falls off. This looks icky!

5. Then the big caterpillar hangs upside down. It wraps itself in a green and gold case.

6. In about two weeks, the case breaks open.

Out comes a monarch butterfly! It is really beautiful!

Henry and the Fox

by Giovanni De Carlo
illustrated by Karen A. Jerome

Henry and the Fox

by Giovanni De Carlo
illustrated by Karen A. Jerome

Strategy Focus

Who will keep Henry from feeling lonely this summer? Stop every two or three pages to **summarize** what you have read.

Think About the Selection

1. Where does Henry live?

2. At the beginning of the story, Henry feels he might be too lonely. How does he feel at the end of the story?

Compare and Contrast

Copy the chart on a piece of paper. Mark how Henry and the fox are the same and different.

	Henry	Fox
Likes raspberries.	✓	✓
Was caught in a trap.	?	?
Has a wheelchair.	?	?
Became friends.	?	?

23

H enry lived on a farm. All his school friends lived in town. Now school was out for summer. Henry hoped he would not be too lonely on the farm.

The fox was bigger now. She was not alone. She had two pups!

Henry grinned as he watched them play. This summer, he would have *three* fox friends.

Henry and the Fox/Selection 2

Henry liked to wheel all over the farm.
He fed the chickens. He picked up eggs.
He watched the silverfish in the stream.

Henry and the Fox/Selection 2

Spring came again. The skies got blue. The wind got warmer.

At the raspberry patch, something caught Henry's eye.

There was his friend, the fox!

Of all the places on the farm, Henry liked the raspberry patch best. He went there every day. One day, something caught his eye. A tiny red fox was standing near him.

15D

Henry didn't see the fox again that summer.

Fall came. The sky got gray. The winds grew colder.

Soon winter snows covered the raspberry patch.

Henry and the Fox/Selection 2

Henry sat very still. The fox was trying to eat the bright, red berries in the bushes. "She looks too small," thought Henry. "She must be hungry."

The fox ran out. She stopped and looked at Henry as if to say, "Thank you!" Then she ran into the woods.

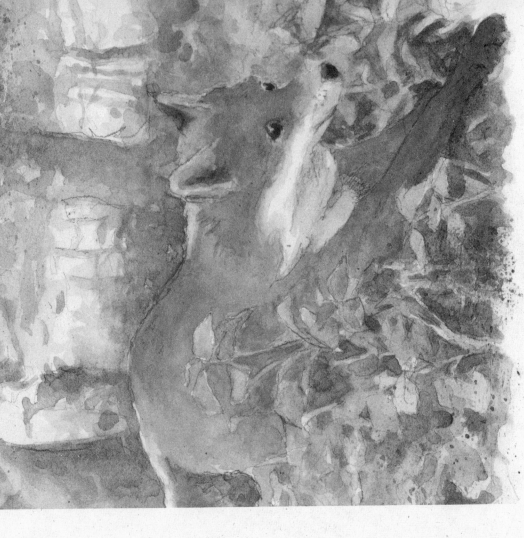

Slowly Henry picked one raspberry. He tossed it to the fox. She ran off before the berry hit the ground. Henry waited, but the fox didn't come back.

The fox saw Henry. She stopped crying. She came to the door and looked up at him. Henry leaned down and opened the door.

Henry and the Fox/Selection 2

The next day, the fox *did* come back. Henry tossed a raspberry again. This time she ate it. Henry tossed another, and another.

Henry saw a wire box. It was a trap. Inside the trap was the little red fox! She had been making the sound.

Every day, the fox came back. She ate all the raspberries Henry tossed to her.

"I've made a new friend!" thought Henry.

19D

Henry followed the sound past the raspberry patch. He followed the sound into the woods. The sound got louder.

32

Henry and the Fox/Selection 2

For three weeks, Henry visited with the little fox. Then one day she didn't show up. She didn't come the next day, either.

One day, Henry was wheeling across the farm. He heard something. It sounded like crying.

THE UPSIDE-DOWN ELEPHANT

by Yoko Mia Hirano

illustrated by Jean & Mou-sien Tseng

THE UPSIDE-DOWN ELEPHANT

by Yoko Mia Hirano
illustrated by Jean & Mou-sien Tseng

Strategy Focus

What can Nilu do when he finds an elephant that is upside down? **Monitor** your reading to make sure each part of the story makes sense.

Responding

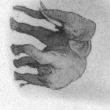

THINK ABOUT THE SELECTION

1   What does Nilu find in the ditch?

2   How do you feel about the people helping the elephant? Why is it a good thing or a bad thing?

MAKING JUDGMENTS

Copy this chart on a piece of paper. Then complete it to show a judgment you made about Nilu.

What the Character Does	What I Think About It	Why I Think This
Mr. Ghatak brings a crane and chains.	Mr. Ghatak is kind because he wants to help the elephant.	It is a good thing to help animals who are in trouble.
Nilu jumps into the ditch to push the elephant.	?	?

Nilu (NEE-loo) looked out at the sun. He had the whole day to play in the forest! The forest was his favorite place. He jumped out of bed.

23D

Everybody walked the elephant back to its home. Nilu felt happy.

"I hope we'll see him again," Nilu joked. "Right side up, next time!"

THE UPSIDE-DOWN ELEPHANT/Selection 3

After breakfast, Nilu walked quickly through his neighborhood. He hoped his little sister wouldn't follow him.

The elephant stood up. Everybody cheered!

Nilu's sister asked, "Where will the elephant go?"

"Deep into the forest," said Nilu. "We'll take him."

Soon Nilu was at the forest. He looked for the drawings he had made in the dirt last week. They were gone. Then he heard a noise.

Nilu jumped into the muddy ditch. He pushed the elephant as hard as he could. Other people jumped in too. Very slowly, they pushed the elephant out.

54

THE UPSIDE-DOWN ELEPHANT/Selection 3

Had Nilu's little sister come after him? She couldn't have. There was no place for her to hide. Then Nilu saw the big ditch nearby.

Snap! The second chain broke. Mr. Ghatak reached for the third chain.

"That won't work either," thought Nilu. "We need to try something else."

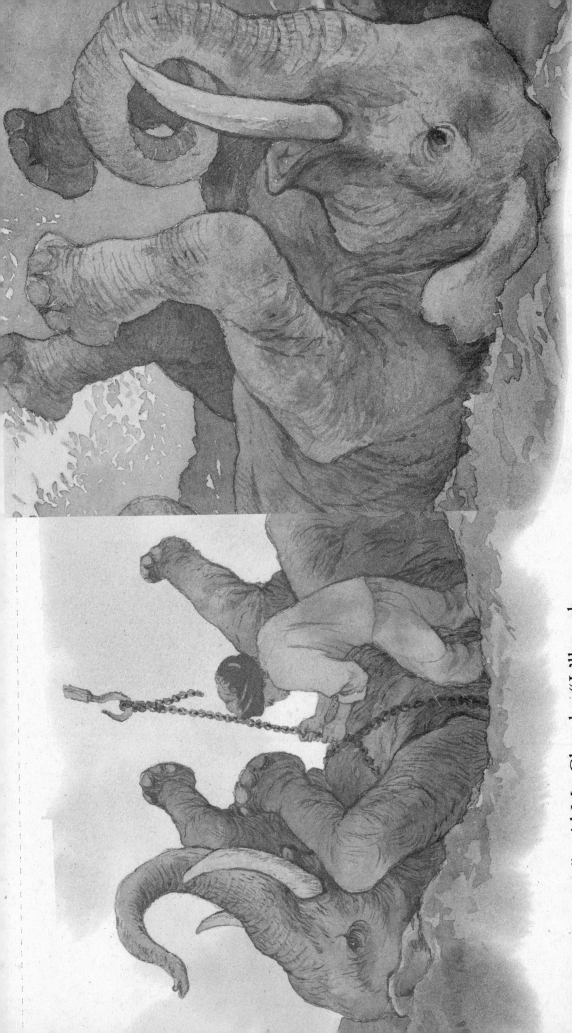

Nilu walked to the side of the ditch. Suddenly he jumped back. There was an elephant in the ditch! The elephant was upside down!

45

"Don't worry," said Mr. Ghatak. "It'll work this time, for sure!" He put another chain around the elephant.

Again, Nilu held his breath.

52

The elephant didn't look very happy. Now and then, it moved its big legs in the air.

Nilu ran home to tell his parents.

Mr. Ghatak put one of the chains around the elephant. Nilu held his breath as Mr. Ghatak raised the crane.

Snap! The chain broke. Everyone sighed.

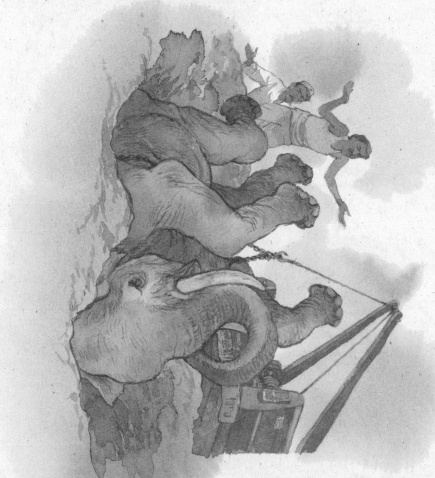

Soon everybody in the neighborhood knew about the elephant.

Many people went with Nilu back to the ditch. The elephant was still there. It was still upside down.

29D

Mr. Ghatak came back. He was in a small truck with a crane and three strong chains. "Now we can pull the elephant out," he said.

50

THE UPSIDE-DOWN ELEPHANT/Selection 3

Uncle Shardul (Shar-DOOL) looked worried. "An elephant needs to stand on its feet or it will die," he said. "We'll have to pull him out."

"But how?" cried Nilu. No one seemed to know.

Suddenly Mr. Ghatak (Gah-TACK) smiled. "I have an idea!" he said. "I'll be back."

HOUGHTON MIFFLIN

Reading

A Legacy of Literacy

Voyagers

THEME 5

Voyagers

Reader's Library Selection 1, *The Golden Land*
To accompany Anthology Selection 1, *Across the Wide Dark Sea:*
  The Mayflower Journey
Comprehension Skill: Making Inferences

Reader's Library Selection 2, *Brothers are Forever*
To accompany Anthology Selection 2, *Yunmi and Halmoni's Trip*
Comprehension Skill: Predicting Outcomes

Reader's Library Selection 3, *Iceberg Rescue*
To accompany Anthology Selection 3, *Trapped by the Ice:*
  Shackleton's Amazing Antarctic Adventure
Comprehension Skill: Text Organization

The Golden Land

by Lee S. Justice

illustrated by Marni Backer

The Golden Land

by Lee S. Justice
illustrated by Marni Backer

Strategy Focus

Samuel and his family are on their way to America. As you read, ask yourself **questions** about their trip.

Responding

Think About the Selection

1. How long has it been since Samuel last saw his father?

2. Why do you think the people cheered and wept when they saw the Statue of Liberty?

Making Inferences

Copy this chart on a piece of paper. Read each story clue, and write the inference it suggests.

Story Clue	Inference
Samuel held onto Mama's coat as if he were a little boy.	Samuel was a little scared.
Samuel realized that Mama had not smiled for a very long time.	?
Papa looked different now. But his hug felt the same to Samuel.	?

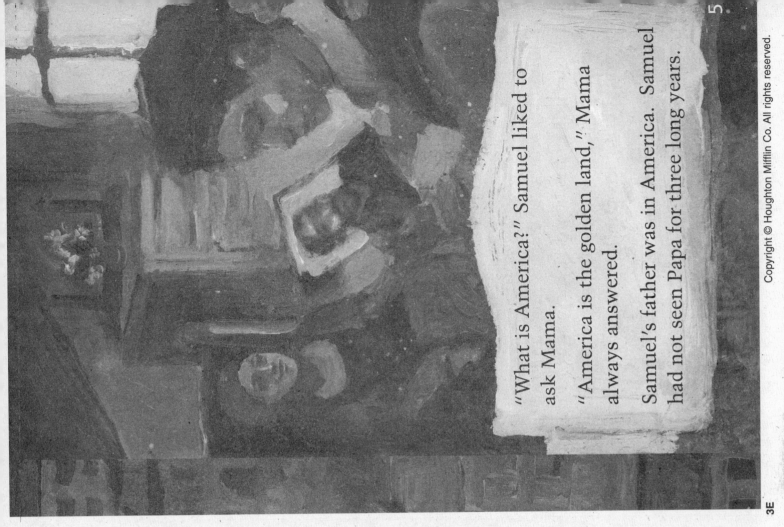

"What is America?" Samuel liked to ask Mama.

"America is the golden land," Mama always answered.

Samuel's father was in America. Samuel had not seen Papa for three long years.

3E

Papa looked different now. But his hug felt just the way Samuel remembered it.

The Golden Land/Selection 1

Samuel remembered Papa's hugs and the soft feeling of his beard. Papa was working in America. He was saving money so that he could bring his family to the golden land.

One day, a letter came. Papa had sent the tickets at last!

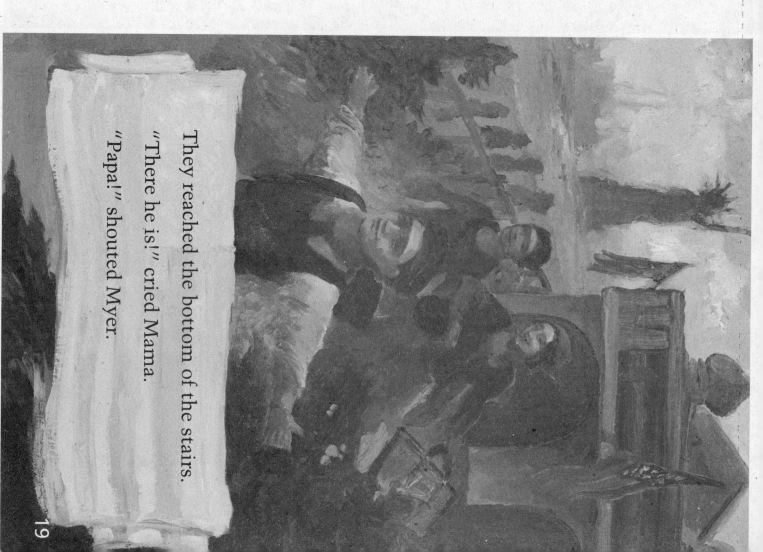

They reached the bottom of the stairs.

"There he is!" cried Mama.

"Papa!" shouted Myer.

Mama cried. Grandmother cried. Samuel cried. Even Samuel's older brother, Myer, wiped tears from his face.

They were all happy. Yet there was an empty feeling, too. Grandmother was not coming with them.

5E

At last, Mama's turn came. She answered the questions. Then a man pointed her to a stairway.

"We are in America now," Mama said with a smile. Samuel realized that Mama had not smiled for a very long time.

18

The Golden Land/Selection 1

A wagon took the travelers to the train. Samuel watched the family's house get smaller and smaller. Then the road curved. The house was gone.

They waited in line. They waited on benches. Samuel hopped on one foot. Then he hopped on the other. So much waiting!

When their name was called, Mama would have to answer questions. Samuel helped her get ready.

Samuel had always wanted to ride on a train.
It was bumpier and noisier than he had
thought it would be.

The houses and fields came, then went.
At last, the train reached a busy port.

7E

The Golden Land/Selection 1

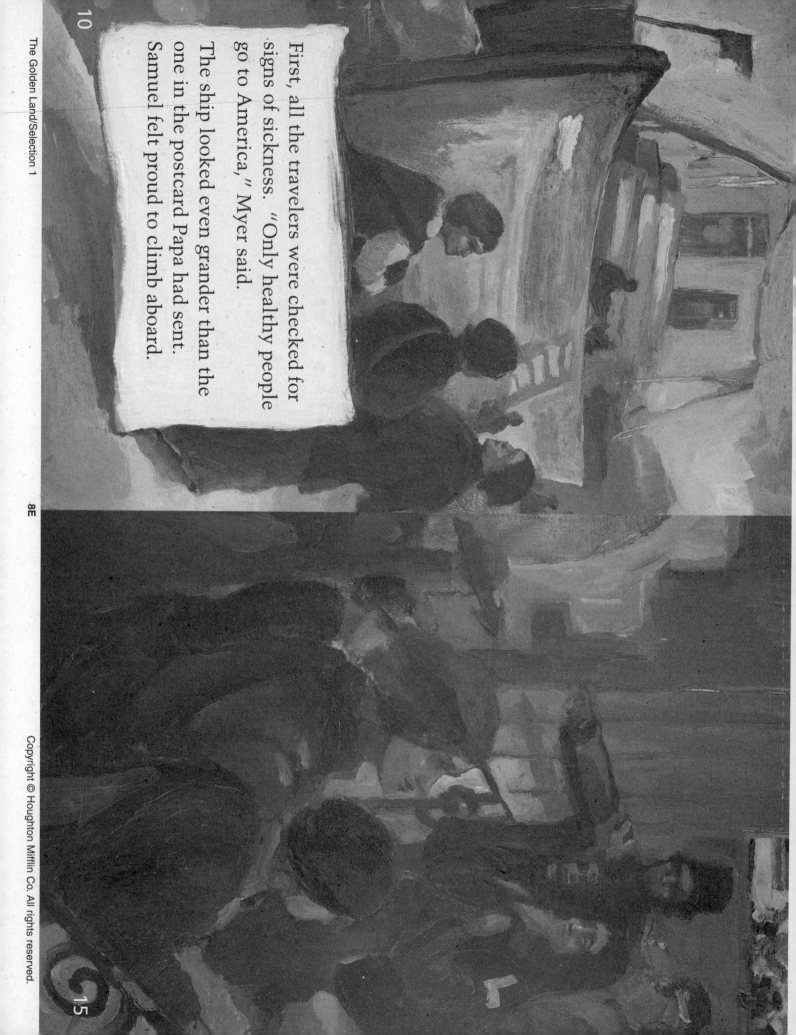

First, all the travelers were checked for signs of sickness. "Only healthy people go to America," Myer said.

The ship looked even grander than the one in the postcard Papa had sent. Samuel felt proud to climb aboard.

During the long boat ride, Samuel played tag on the deck and listened to people talking. They spoke all kinds of languages. Samuel liked to listen to the strange sounds.

A ferry took them to a big building. Inside were so many people! Samuel held onto Mama's coat as if he were a little boy.

They waited in line. Men put chalk marks on people's coats. A chalk mark might mean that someone was ill and would have to stay there until he or she got better.

"Look strong and healthy!" Mama said. Samuel pushed his chest out. Myer stood tall. No chalk marks!

14

Samuel felt lucky that he did not get seasick like Myer. "Ooooh," poor Myer moaned. Mama held Myer's head.

They slept below with many other passengers. It was stuffy and smelled bad.

"Soon we will be in America," Mama said over and over.

12

On the tenth day, everyone ran to the top deck. "Look!" they shouted. "There she is!" People cheered and wept.

A man picked Samuel up so he could see. Samuel blinked at the golden sunlight gleaming off the statue's crown.

"She is welcoming us," Mama said softly.

13

BROTHERS are FOREVER

by Marcy Haber

illustrated by Gail Piazza

11E

BROTHERS are FOREVER

by Marcy Haber
illustrated by Gail Piazza

Strategy Focus

Max visits his brother at college in England. As you read, **predict** what will happen during the visit.

12E

Responding

Think About the Selection

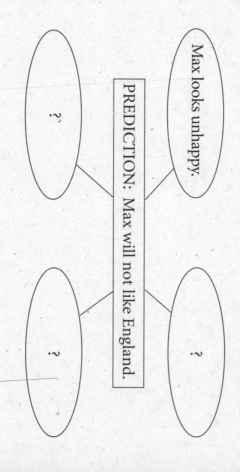

1 Where did Max and his parents go to visit Russ?

2 Did Max like how Russ had changed? Why?

What Do You Predict?

Copy this web on a piece of paper. Read the prediction. Then write details from the story that support it.

Max looks unhappy.

PREDICTION: Max will not like England.

?

?

?

"Yahoo!" Max shouted. "We're going to London! I can't wait to see Russ."

23

"Sure I do!" Max said. "That'd be great! I mean, jolly good!"

38

It was a long trip from New York to London. Max could not sit still. He had so much to tell his older brother. It had been four whole months since they had seen each other. Would Russ even know who he was? Max had gotten a lot taller.

"You mean it?" asked Max.

"Of course," said Russ. "And another thing. Ian and I are running a football camp here this summer. I mean soccer camp. Well, you know. Mom and Dad said it's okay for you to come. But I guess you don't like it here."

At last the plane landed. Russ was there to meet his family.

"Hey, Peanut!" Russ yelled to Max. Max had always hated being called Peanut. But this time he didn't mind. Russ had missed him. Max could tell.

25

"I do have new friends," said Russ. "And I do like it here. But you're wrong about not needing you. Brothers are forever. Even when they get too tall to be called Peanut."

36

BROTHERS are FOREVER/Selection 2

15E

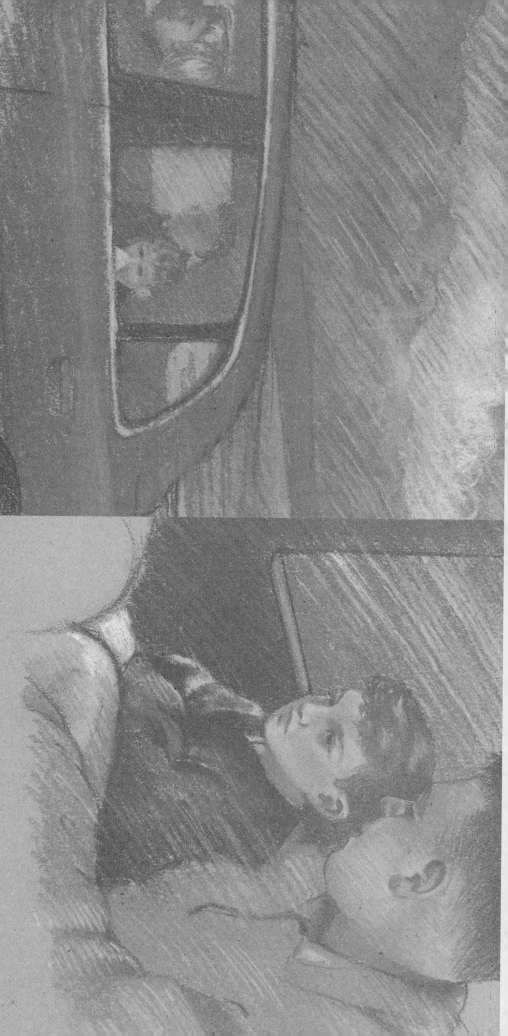

"I have so much to show you," said Russ. He spoke with an accent. "Wait till you meet my college chums!"

"Chums?" thought Max.

At first, Max said nothing. Then he blurted out, "You used to be *my* roommate. Now you have a flatmate. You're a soccer hero. Or a football hero. Or whatever. And you talk funny! You don't need a brother anymore."

Then he added, "And why did you stop calling me Peanut and start calling me Max?"

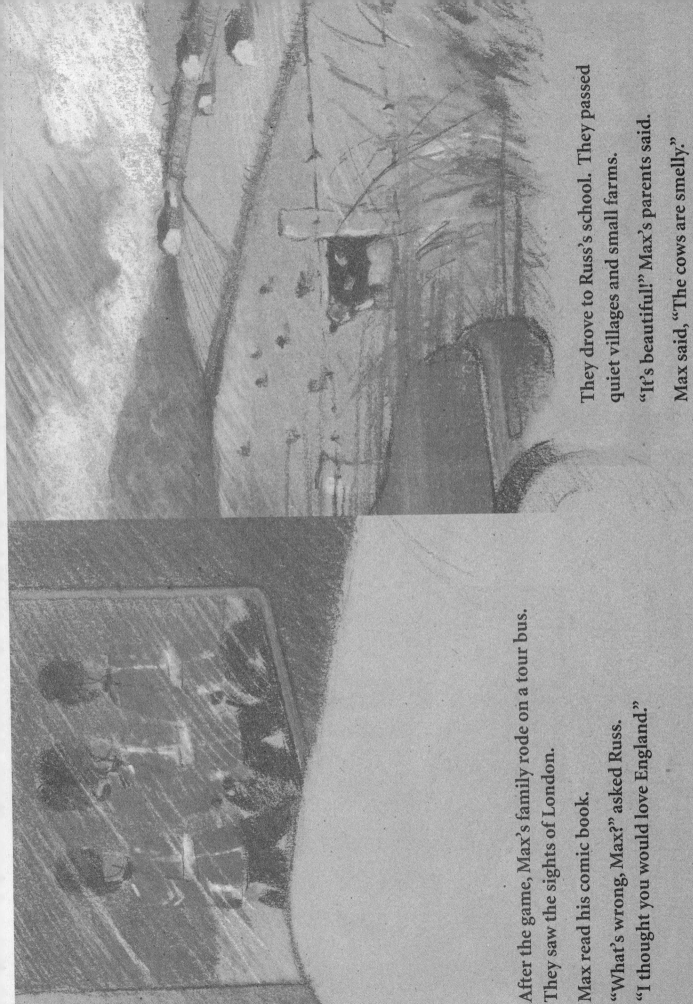

27

They drove to Russ's school. They passed quiet villages and small farms.

"It's beautiful!" Max's parents said.

Max said, "The cows are smelly."

34

After the game, Max's family rode on a tour bus. They saw the sights of London.

Max read his comic book.

"What's wrong, Max?" asked Russ.

"I thought you would love England."

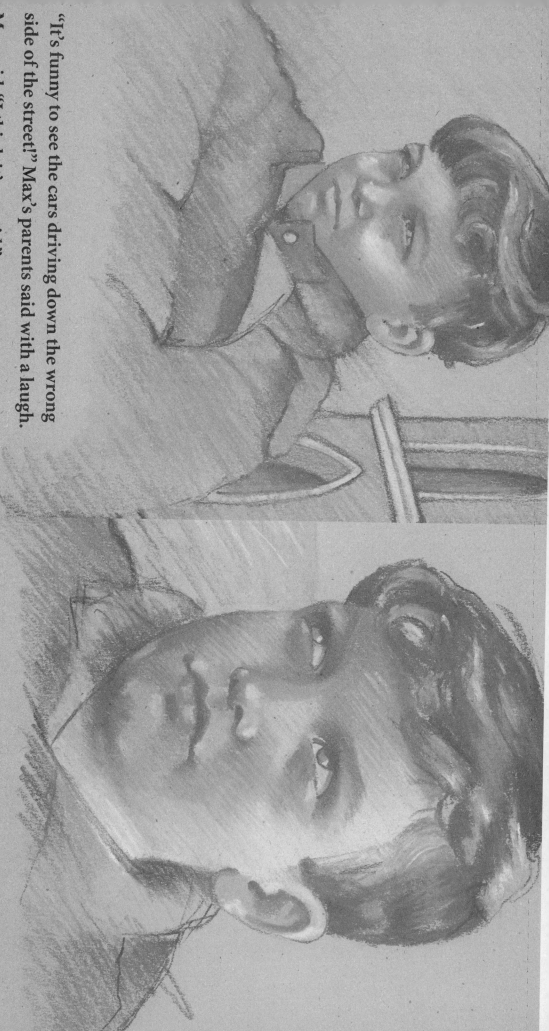

"It's funny to see the cars driving down the wrong side of the street!" Max's parents said with a laugh.

Max said, "I think it's stupid."

Russ started getting mad. "It isn't stupid, Max," he answered. "It's just different."

"Your accent is different *and* stupid," Max said under his breath.

Later, they went to Russ's football game. Russ scored a goal. The crowd cheered.

"Russ is doing great in school," thought Max. "He won't ever want to come home."

BROTHERS are FOREVER/Selection 2

18E

They stopped at a large stone building.

"This is where I live," said Russ.

His parents said, "It looks like a castle!"

Max shrugged.

29

Russ showed his family around the college. He stopped to talk to his new friends. He kept using strange words. "Jolly good!" he'd say, or "Right-o!"

"Dumb-o," Max said to himself.

32

19E

They walked to Russ's room. "This is my flatmate, Ian," said Russ.

"He doesn't look flat to me," Max said.

"In London, an apartment is called a *flat*," Russ told him.

"Russ and I play football together," Ian said.

"He tells me you're not bad at it, either."

"Russ doesn't play football! And neither do I! We play soccer," Max answered.

"In England, football *is* soccer," said Ian.

Max felt as if he were on another planet.

Iceberg Rescue

by Sarah Amada

illustrated by S. Saelig Gallagher

21E

Iceberg Rescue

by Sarah Amada

illustrated by S. Saelig Gallagher

Strategy Focus

How can an iceberg help Louise free her ship? As you read, **monitor** your understanding and reread to **clarify** details.

Responding

Think About the Selection

1 What was Louise Arner Boyd doing near the coast of northeast Greenland?

2 What is a good way to understand how *Iceberg Rescue* is organized?

Text Organizers

A heading gives information about part of a story. Copy this chart on a piece of paper. Then write the heading to go with each picture.

What's in the Picture?	Heading
Louise Arner Boyd watching the icy coastline	World of Ice
a ship stuck in the mud	?
the crew looking happy as the ship breaks free of the ice	?

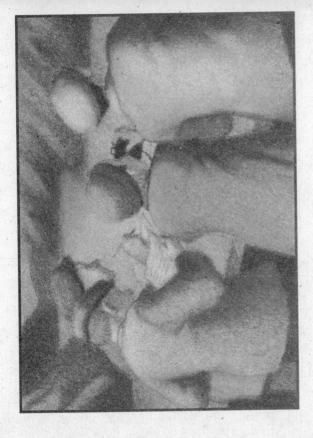

World of Ice

It was the winter of 1933. Explorer Louise Arner Boyd and her team had been at sea for six weeks. They were taking pictures and making maps of the wild and dangerous coast of northeast Greenland.

23E

Louise took more photos as they pulled away from the mountains of ice. She was relieved to be free, but she knew she would be back to explore this place again.

Iceberg Rescue/Selection 3

Their ship, the *Veslekari*, moved slowly toward Nunatak Glacier. Louise stared up at the mountain of ice.

The water around them was filled with ice. After three tries they broke through the ice and moved out to sea.

55

She took many photos and wrote down every detail she saw. All her information would be very useful for understanding this mysterious part of the world.

Free!

The captain ordered his crew to start the ship's engines. What a noise! The motors roared. The crank squeaked as it pulled on the cable. The ship lifted off the mud! Thanks to Louise's good idea, the *Veslekari* was free!

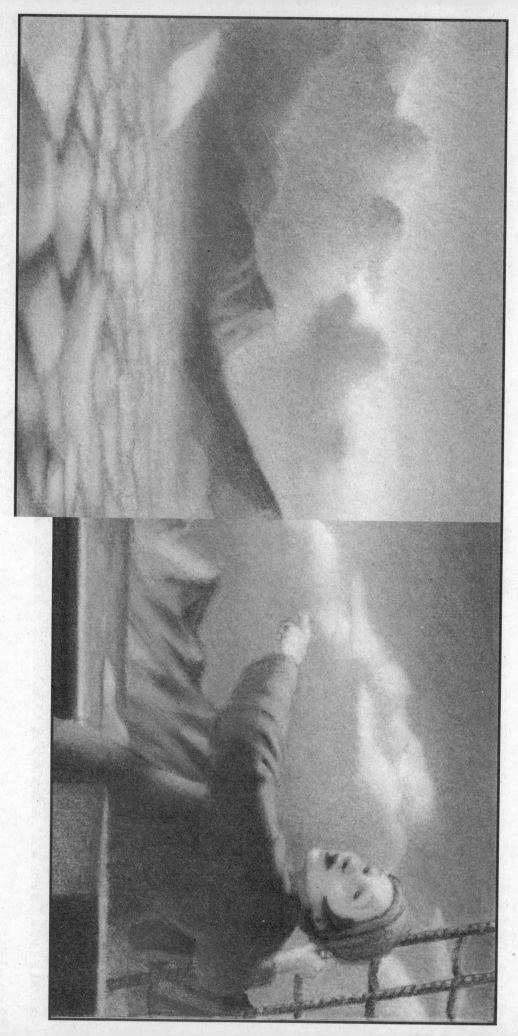

Stuck!

All at once, the ship shook. The shock threw Louise and the others to their knees. The front of the ship made a loud sound. The *Veslekari* had run aground.

Then Louise saw a big iceberg floating toward the ship. She had an idea. The ship's crew tied a cable around the iceberg. Then they pulled on the cable. The cable pulled on the iceberg.

The captain yelled, "Reverse the engines!"
The ship's crew ran the motors at full speed.
But the *Veslekari* did not move.

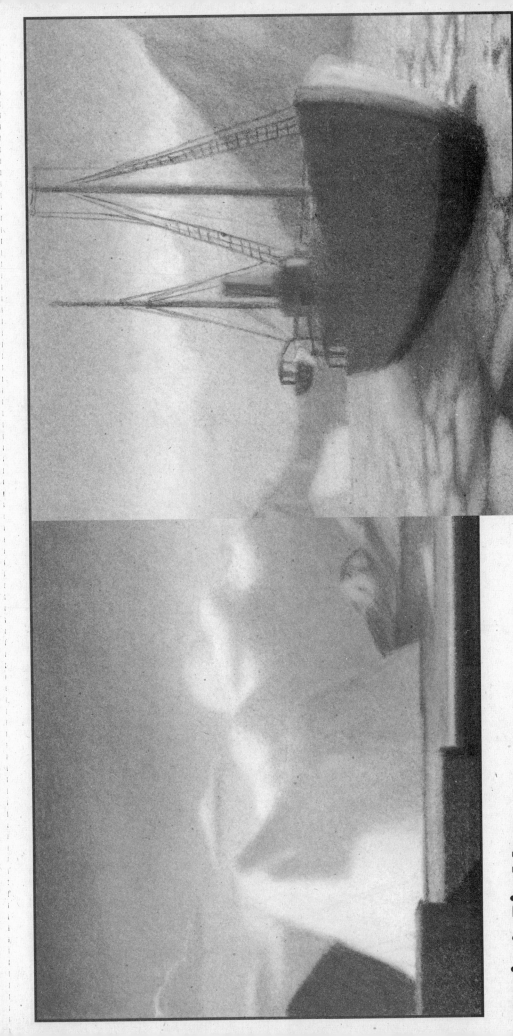

Louise's Big Idea

The tide came in and went out again.
The *Veslekari* was still stuck.

52

No Way Out

Now they were stuck, and it was the middle of winter. Louise knew that northeast Greenland was not a good place to spend a winter. Many explorers had died here, cold and hungry.

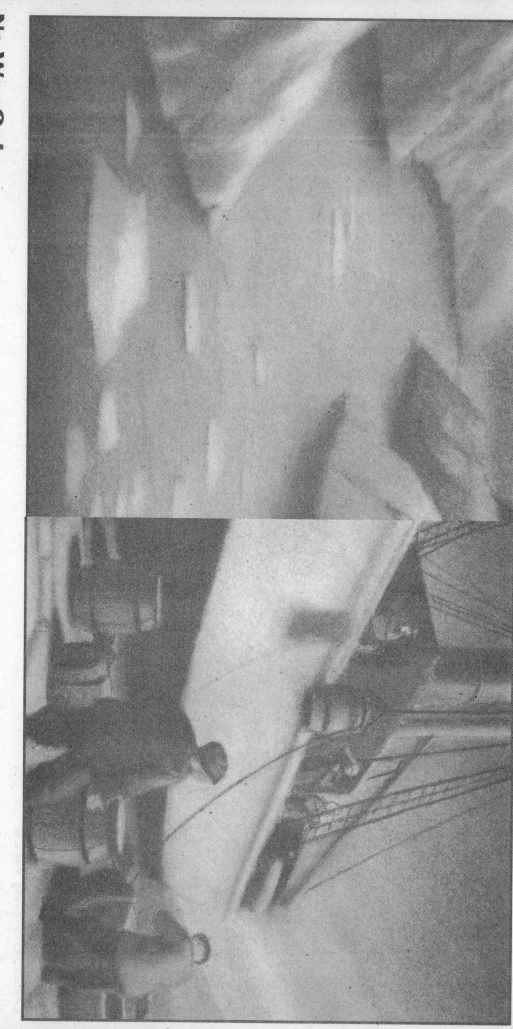

They took three small boats off the ship. Then they took off almost four tons of oil and gas. Finally, they threw fifteen tons of coal overboard.

28E

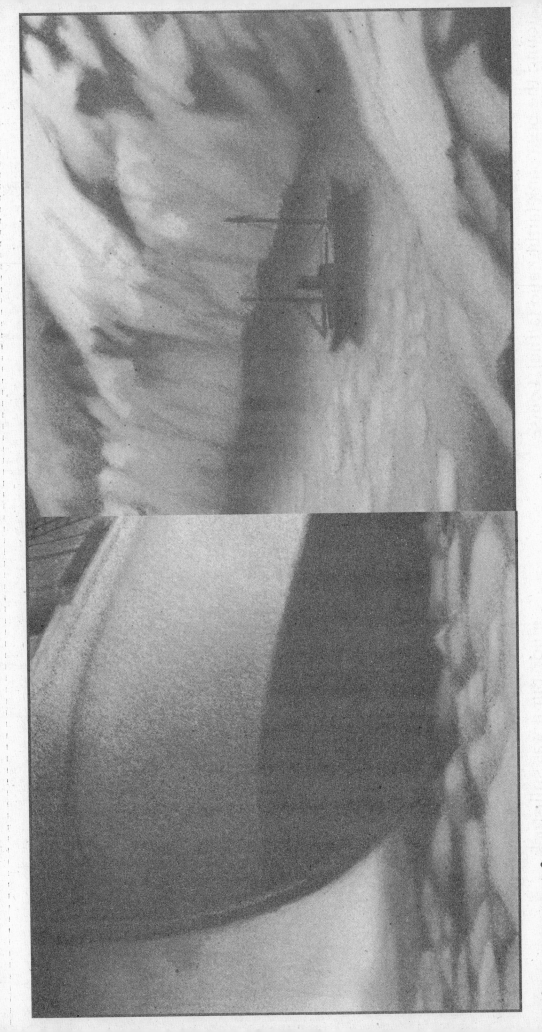

Louise also knew that there were no other ships close by. She and her team had to save themselves.

Time for Action

The *Veslekari* was too heavy to float off the mud, even when the tide came back up and water again surrounded the ship. Louise and the others had to make it lighter.

The tide was getting lower. As the water level around the boat sank farther and farther, Louise waited and watched. She was worried. She knew that the ship might tip to one side in the mud. If it tipped over, the ship's crew would not be able to lift it. The *Veslekari* was very, very heavy.

Luckily, the ship stayed upright in the mud. But it was still stuck.

Smart
Solutions

THEME 6

Smart Solutions

Reader's Library Selection 1, *Tall Tony*
To accompany Anthology Selection 1, *Pepita Talks Twice*
Comprehension Skill: Problem Solving

Reader's Library Selection 2, *A Little Bit Hotter Can't Hurt*
To accompany Anthology Selection 2, *Poppa's New Pants*
Comprehension Skill: Drawing Conclusions

Reader's Library Selection 3, *The Dive*
To accompany Anthology Selection 3, *Ramona Quimby, Age 8*
Comprehension Skill: Making Generalizations

Tall Tony

by Lucy Floyd

illustrated by
Diane Hearn

Tall Tony

by Lucy Floyd
illustrated by
Diane Hearn

Strategy Focus

Tony is the tallest boy in his class, and sometimes that's a bother. As you read, **evaluate** how well the words and pictures work together to tell Tony's story.

2F

Think About the Selection

1. Who is taller than his teacher?

2. What problem does Alex have? How does he solve it?

Tony Finds Solutions

Copy the web on a piece of paper. Write Tony's problem in the circle. Write solutions to Tony's problem that you read about in the story.

```
         PROBLEM
            ?

Solution      Solution      Solution
He thinks        ?             ?
about
saying something
to the class.
```

21

Tony was very tall. In fact, he was the tallest person in his class. He was even taller than the teacher, Ms. Bell.

"The basketball is on top of the shelf," said Mr. Sams. "Will you please reach up and get it for me?"

20

Tony didn't mind being tall. He liked being able to reach things nobody else could reach. Tony was always reaching up high for something.

"Now we can start practice," said Mr. Sams.

"But first, there's one thing I need you to do, Tony."

"Name it, Coach," said Tony happily.

5F

"Me!" said Tony, standing very straight to look as tall as he could. "How about me?"

"YES!" everybody yelled. "CAPTAIN TONY!"

18   Tall Tony/Selection 1

"Tony, I need that book on the top shelf. Will you please get it for me?" Alex asked.

Tony got the book.

"The player who knows all about basketball!" said Alex.

"The player who is super fast!" said May.

"The player who is a good leader!" said Jim.

"The player who shoots lots of baskets!" said Anna.

"Who is that player?" asked Mr. Sams.

17

"Tony, it's hot in here. Will you please open that window?" May asked.

Tony opened the window.

In the gym, everyone gathered around Mr. Sams, the basketball coach.

"A basketball team needs a captain," he said.

"Now, who do you think it should be?"

7F

"Tony, I want this elephant picture at the top of the board. Will you please tack it up for me?" Ms. Bell asked.

Tony tacked up the picture.

So Tony raised his hand.

"Yes, Tony?" said Ms. Bell.

"I want to say something to the class," Tony said.

"Later," said Ms. Bell. "Right now it's time to go to the gym for basketball."

11

"Tony, I forgot to write *Canada* at the top of this map," Anna said. "Will you please write it for me?"

Tony wrote *Canada.*

14

One day, Tony got tired of doing all the reaching. "I'm going to shrink myself," he thought. "Being tall is driving me CRAZY. I've got to say something about it."

Tall Tony/Selection 1

9F

Day after day, Tony had to do things because he was the tallest person in his class.

Who had to draw stars at the top of the mural?

Tony did.

Who had to measure the clock AND the door for math lesson?

Tony did.

A Little Bit 'Hotter' Can't Hurt

By Joanna Korba

Illustrated by Bethann Thornburgh

A Little Bit 'Hotter' Can't Hurt

By Joanna Korba
Illustrated by Bethann Thornburgh

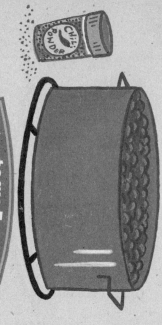

Strategy Focus

When Lindy visits Texas, Aunt Birdie makes chili. As you read, **predict** how warm a welcome the chili will be.

Responding

Think About the Selection

1 What food does Aunt Birdie say she made just for Lindy?

2 What three clues let you know that there is a lot of chili powder in the chili?

Use Clues to Draw a Conclusion

Copy the chart on a piece of paper. Then complete the chart by writing two more clues about the weather that day.

Clues

?
Everyone sits out front to talk.
?

Conclusion

The story takes place on a hot day.

"WE WILL BE LANDING IN TEN MINUTES . . ."

23

And from that day on, everyone in Lindy's family liked chili that was a little bit hotter.

Now that can't hurt, can it?

38

". . . in Texas!" Lindy Parker finished.

"Aunt Birdie and Uncle Buster are so glad we're coming," said her mother. "Birdie made some chili just for you."

"Well! It's a good thing I didn't add some chili powder," said Uncle Buster. "Our smoke alarms would go off!"

"You know what?" said Aunt Birdie. "I like it this way!"

"Is it hot like your chili?" Lindy asked.

"I *love* your chili!"

"The Grigsbees like their chili mild," her mother said. "But be nice, honey. Pretend you like it."

"But I only put in a little more chili powder!" Aunt Birdie cried.

"Oh, dear," said Lindy's mother. "So did I!"

"Oh, no! Me too!" cried Lindy.

A Little Bit Hotter Can't Hurt/Selection 2

"We're so tickled to see y'all!" cried Uncle Buster.

"I made some chili just for you, Lindy. I know you love chili," said Aunt Birdie. "Now give me some sugar!"

Lindy laughed and planted a kiss on her aunt's cheek.

Everyone took a bite of chili. Everyone's eyes got larger. You see, the chili wasn't a *little* bit hotter. . . .

It . . . was . . . a . . . LOT . . . hotter!

Lindy's mother whispered to her sister, "Lindy likes hot chili, Birdie. Can you make yours a bit hotter?"

"Well, sure," said Aunt Birdie. "A little bit hotter can't hurt."

17F

Everyone helped set the table. Then Aunt Birdie brought out the giant bowl of chili.

Lindy was worried. She had only added a *little* bit of chili powder. Would anyone notice?

A Little Bit Hotter Can't Hurt/Selection 2

18F

It was a lazy afternoon in the Texas sun. Everyone sat out front to talk. Aunt Birdie went inside to get some iced tea.

Lindy washed her hands. Then she saw the chili and the chili powder.

"I'll make the chili just a little bit hotter," she thought. "I don't want to upset Aunt Birdie. But a little bit hotter can't hurt."

The chili was cooking. Aunt Birdie walked over and lifted the cover. Then she reached for the chili powder.

"I'll add a little for Lindy," she said to herself. "A little bit hotter can't hurt."

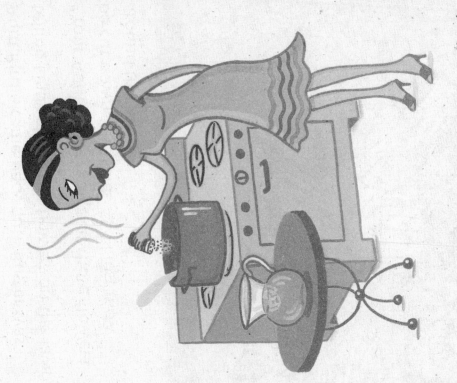

Later, Lindy played with the hens. Aunt Birdie and Uncle Buster kept them as pets.

"We will be eating dinner soon, Lindy," her mother said. "Give your hands a good washing."

32

A Little Bit Hotter Can't Hurt/Selection 2

Aunt Birdie came back out. Buster was telling Lindy about the flowers on the lawn.

"Your Aunt Birdie won't let those flowers be cut down," he said. "So I just mow around them!"

After a while, Lindy's mother went to get a sweet potato pie from the oven. She saw the chili — and the chili powder.

"I'll make it a little bit hotter for Lindy," she thought. "Birdie said she didn't mind."

The Dive

by Susan Delaney

illustrated by Michael Chesworth

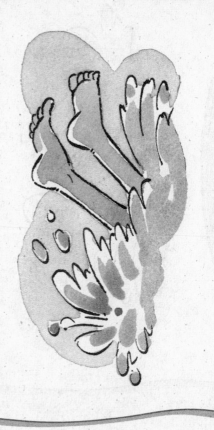

The Dive

by Susan Delaney
illustrated by Michael Chesworth

Strategy Focus

Christy won't admit it, but she is scared to learn to dive. As you read, stop now and then to **summarize** what you've read so far.

Think About the Selection

1 Who could do a real dive?

2 The story says that Christy waited all week for Megan's party. Tell what you think *all week* means.

What Does It Mean?

Copy the chart on a piece of paper. Write what each generalization from the story really means.

Generalization	What It Means
Christy showed *everyone* how to do a split jump.	Christy showed everyone at Megan's party how to do a split jump.
Diving is silly anyway, she thought.	?
"Diving is easy," Nathan replied.	?

Christy had waited all week for Megan's party at the public pool. And it was turning out to be lots of fun.

23F

Nathan raised his hands, and Christy raised her hands. Christy's mother blew air out her nose, and Christy blew air out her nose. Sara smiled. She dived in. And Christy dived in right after her.

56

Christy showed everyone how to do a split jump.
She was just about to do a twist in the air. Then
Sara arrived.

Sara could dive. And everyone wanted to learn.

Then Christy's mom, and Nathan, and Sara all
stood beside her at the edge of the pool. Suddenly,
Christy didn't feel afraid!

For the rest of the day, the pool was filled with the sound of the girls hitting the water on their bellies like little whales. By the end of the day, everyone had tried to dive. Everyone but Christy.

"The first time I tried diving, I was really scared," said Sara, as if she could read Christy's mind. "But finally I closed my eyes and just dived right in. It was easy after that."

The Dive/Selection 3

"Hi Christy," Sara said. "Want to practice diving together? Then maybe you can show me your split jump."

"Umm, okay," Christy said. She was still afraid.

When she got home, Christy lay on her bed, thinking about the party. Diving is silly anyway, she thought. Who wants to plop into the water headfirst, like a frog?

But she started doing pretend dives anyway. She puffed out her cheeks and swung her arms back. Just then, her brother walked in.

When he saw Christy, he began to laugh. "What are you, some kind of blowfish?" he asked.

KEEP OUT
this means
you,
NATHAN
!!!

The next day, Christy, her mom, and Nathan headed for the town pool. When they got there, Sara was waiting for them.

The Dive/Selection 3

Christy gave him a look that said, "Very funny." Then she asked, "Hey, Nathan, do you know how to dive?"

"Sure. Diving is easy," Nathan replied. He put his hands together and jumped onto Christy's bed. Then Nathan saw the hurt look on her face.

"I can help you," he said. Nathan showed her how to hold her arms and bend her legs.

Christy thought her mom looked like a snorting dragon when she blew air out her nose. Christy decided to practice in front of a mirror before she tried it in public.

"You have to blow air out your nose," her mother said. She showed Christy what to do.

29F

The Dive/Selection 3

Before dinner, Christy told her mom about the party. "Sara ruined it," she said. "She thinks she's so great because she knows how to dive."

Her mom gave her a funny look. "I thought you liked Sara," she said.

"I guess she's okay," Christy admitted. "But I don't like diving."

"Did you even try?" asked her mom.

"I can't!" Christy whined. "I hold my nose when I jump. You can't hold your nose and dive."